Fun
French Fairy Tale Plays

Learn Language Confidently Through Drama

Dorothy M Hamilton

Brilliant
PUBLICATIONS

Publisher's Information

We hope you and your pupils enjoy the plays in this book. Brilliant Publications publishes many other books to support, inspire and challenge primary school teachers and pupils. To find out more details on any of our titles please log onto our website www.brilliantpublications.co.uk.

Learn French with Luc et Sophie
Brilliant French Information Books
Bistro Escargot
12 Petites Pièces à Jouer
Chantez Plus Fort

Published by Brilliant Publications Limited
Unit 10,
Sparrow Hall Farm,
Edlesborough,
Dunstable,
Bedfordshire,
LU6 2ES

Website: www.brilliantpublications.co.uk
E-mail: info@brilliantpublications.co.uk
Tel: 01525 222292
Fax: 01525 222720

The name 'Brilliant Publications' and the logo are registered trade marks.

Written by Dorothy M Hamilton
Illustrated by Molly Sage
Cover illustration by Molly Sage
Production of CD recordings by Hart McLeod Limited

© 2017 Dorothy M Hamilton and Brilliant Publications
The Rock and Roll version of Frère Jacques (page 48) is used with permission from Matt Maxwell and AIM Language Learning (www.aimlanguagelearning.com).
Printed ISBN: 978-1-78317-245-0
First published 2017
10 9 8 7 6 5 4 3 2 1

Contents

Play	Theme	Language focus	Actors needed	CD Track	Page
Cendrillon	Love	Expressing opinions. Everyday language useful for home activities. Simple phrases in the present tense.	10	1	6–12
La Petite Poule Rousse	Animals and actions. Food. Table manners	Simple phrases in present tense. Verbs with 'je'. Everyday language useful for mealtimes.	12+	2	13–18
Pauvre Papa Noël	Making excuses	Weather. Time and dates. Illnesses. Countries. Presents.	11	3	19–23
Boucle d'Or	Food	Useful everyday phrases for preparing and eating food. A few simple phrases in the future and past tense.	13	4	24–30
Rapunzel et la tour Eiffel	Friends. Appearance and personality	Adjectives for describing people. Use of 'être' in the present tense. Comparative adjectives. A few phrases in the future tense using 'aller'.	7	5	31–39
Le Chat Botté	Family	Adjectives, clothes, opinions. Several traditional French songs.	13+	6	40–48
Blanche-Neige et les nains sportifs	Sports and hobbies	Key phrases for sports, hobbies, activities and household chores. Simple phrases in present, past and future tense with 'aller'.	16+	7	49–55
Wendy part en vacances	Holidays	Key phrases about holidays in the present tense, future tense and past tense. Vocabulary for holiday activities, weather, and transport.	12	8	56–64

Les trois petits cochons vont à l'école	School	Phrases about school subjects, likes and dislikes, strengths and weaknesses. Comments about subjects and teachers' personalities. Adjectives. School-bag items. Routine of school day. Time.	10	9	65–72
Dorothée fait les courses	Shopping	Food, clothes, key shopping phrases. Some phrases in the past tense. A fair amount of more advanced sentence structure.	18	10	73–80

English versions

Introduction

These plays have been written to be enjoyed and performed by children and young people learning French. They have all been tried and tested by my pupils who have loved the challenge of learning a French script and performing it to an audience of adults and children. The boost to their confidence and long-term benefit of learning the sentence structures is very valuable.

The plays are mainly adapted from well-known stories making use of the colourful characters that are already known to the audience. Sometimes extra characters have been created or borrowed from other stories in order to involve more pupils. It is noted where certain characters can be omitted without affecting the story which could work better for a smaller group. The stories sometimes vary considerably from the original story and have been given humorous twists where possible. Each story has a language theme such as food or shopping. The linguistic benefit for the pupils is huge as they can learn useful language in a given topic and then use it in a suitable play. This is a fun, but also rigorous activity as the dialogue has to be thoroughly learnt. Pupils will probably need several weeks to rehearse and prepare for the performances which usually last 5–10 minutes. The plays have been placed in approximate order of difficulty with the most challenging ones near the end.

The stage directions are detailed as some of the story and humour is conveyed through the characters' actions. This helps to reduce the amount of vocabulary that must be learnt. Most of the lines are short simple phrases that pupils are likely to know already or need to learn in the wider picture of their linguistic experience. The language and structures in the later plays is more sophisticated however, with some variation in tenses introduced.

There are many traditional French songs included in the plays and some other adapted songs which can be sung to well-known French tunes (usually available to listen to on-line). Do bear in mind that watching the performance is a linguistic experience for the audience too. Younger children might enjoy learning some of the songs beforehand and then recognising them in the performance. It would also help their comprehension if they could have part of the story explained to them in advance. It can be fun for the audience to be given something to listen for in each play to give them a focus.

The audio recordings have been made by highly skilled French actors who really bring the plays to life. Your pupils are sure to enjoy listening to these. Why not challenge them to recognise the animals in La Petite Poule Rousse or guess the hobby of each dwarf in Blanche Neige?

The notes on staging the plays are just suggestions – be creative!

I very much hope you enjoy reading these plays, that your pupils enjoy performing them and that their audiences enjoy watching them!

Cendrillon

Cendrillon

A simple version of Cendrillon (Cinderella) with additional characters including two cheeky mice who can't help teasing Cendrillon but are very fond of her really. With the help of the Bonne Fée (Fairy Godmother), the two stepsisters have to change their ideas!

Theme	
Love	
Language focus	
Expressing opinions. Everyday language useful for home activities. Simple phrases in the present tense.	
Personnages	
Cendrillon	Cinderella
Souris x 2	2 mice
Chat	Cat (optional character. If left out, get Cinderella to tell mice off at the beginning)
Araignée	Spider (optional character, could be left out)
Bonne Fée	Fairy Godmother
Sœurs x 2	2 (ugly) sisters
Prince Charmant	Prince Charming
Facteur	Postman
Costumes and props	
Broom. Plastic baguette, wine bottle, cheese, teacup and saucer. Invitation and envelope. Hairbrush. Cardboard cut-out of carriage. Suitable costumes including smart clothes for ball, work overalls, party shoes and veil. Mouse, cat, spider, horse hoods or masks.	
Staging	
Traditional scenes: by the fire and ball scene. Background dance music would be helpful for the ball scene.	

Scene 1

Cendrillon's (Cinderella's) house

CHAT (Cat) asleep by the fire. ARAIGNÉE (Spider) is annoying CHAT by tickling him. Enter CENDRILLON with a broom sweeping up. She is wearing an old overall with a pretty dress underneath. ARAIGNÉE sees CENDRILLON arrive with her broom and is afraid

ARAIGNÉE:	J'ai peur ... au secours !
CENDRILLON:	Je travaille, je travaille ... . Je suis fatiguée ! *(She looks tired and wipes her hand over her forehead. SOURIS (Mice) come on stage and do the same)*
SOURIS:	Je travaille, je travaille, je suis fatiguée.
CHAT:	Les souris vous êtes très méchantes ! *(CHAT takes broom from CENDRILLON, tells SOURIS off and chases them off stage with the broom)*

SOURIS run off, scared by CHAT, then come back on, sit CENDRILLON down and bring her a cup of tea. CHAT goes back to sleep by fire

SOURIS 1:	Assieds-toi, Cendrillon.
SOURIS 2:	Prends une tasse de thé.
CENDRILLON:	Mmm, c'est bon.

SŒURS (Sisters) arrive, hungry and cross, stamping feet. When CENDRILLON hears them coming, she runs off

SŒUR 1:	J'ai faim.
SŒUR 2:	J'ai soif.
SŒURS:	Cendrillon !
SŒUR 1:	Je voudrais une baguette. *(CENDRILLON runs back and forth bringing items)*
SŒUR 2:	Et du Camembert.
SŒUR 1:	Et du vin rouge !

SOURIS are interested in idea of cheese and wine

SOURIS 1:	Du Camembert ! C'est du fromage ! Miam, miam !
SOURIS 2:	Du vin rouge ? J'adore ça ! *(Pretends to be drunk!)*

CHAT:	Ce n'est pas bon pour les souris ! Miaou !
ARAIGNÉE:	Non, mais c'est très bon pour les araignées ! *(Tries to get the bottle)*

BONNE FÉE (Fairy Godmother) arrives

BONNE FÉE:	*(Knocks)* Toc, toc, toc !
SŒUR 1:	Qui est là ?
SŒUR 2:	Ouvre la porte.
BONNE FÉE:	Bonjour les filles !
SŒUR 1:	Ah non, pas toi ... .
	(In a nasty voice imitating BONNE FÉE) Fais la vaisselle ... .
SŒUR 2:	*(In a nasty voice imitating BONNE FÉE)* Fais la cuisine ... .
BONNE FÉE:	*(Crossly)* Vous êtes très paresseuses et très méchantes !
SŒURS:	Oui, c'est vrai ! *(They sit down and put their feet up, proud of being lazy)*

FACTEUR (Postman) arrives

FACTEUR:	*(Knocks)* Toc, toc, toc.
SŒURS:	Encore ! Cendrillon, ouvre la porte. *(They jump up and then push CENDRILLON to the door)*
CENDRILLON:	Bonjour monsieur.

FACTEUR gives invitation to CENDRILLON

FACTEUR:	Une invitation pour vous.
CENDRILLON:	Merci.

One of the SŒURS snatches it before CENDRILLON has a chance to read it. CENDRILLON moves back

SŒUR 1:	Une invitation ... .
SŒUR 2:	Au bal ... .
SŒUR 1:	Au Palais de Versailles ... .
SŒUR 2:	Samedi ? C'est demain !

SŒURS run around panicking about their hair, clothes, shoes and nails. CENDRILLON runs over and tries to help them get ready

SŒUR 1:	Mes cheveux !
SŒUR 2:	Ma robe !
SŒUR 1:	Mes chaussures !
SŒUR 2:	Mes ongles !

SŒURS go off still fussing and muttering. CENDRILLON sits sadly by the fire, SOURIS try to comfort her

CENDRILLON:	J'adore danser, mais … je ne peux pas aller au bal … .
SOURIS 1:	Ne t'inquiète-pas Cendrillon.

BONNE FÉE stands up with her wand, others look surprised

BONNE FÉE:	Cendrillon, tu vas aller au bal.
CENDRILLON:	Mais, regarde ma robe.
BONNE FÉE:	Allez hop ! *(Waves wand and SOURIS pull overalls from CENDRILLON to reveal pretty dress)*
SOURIS 1:	C'est très jolie.
SOURIS 2:	Tu es belle !

BONNE FÉE waves her wand at SOURIS

BONNE FÉE:	Hop … et hop !

SOURIS, now changed into horses, 'gallop' around the stage and fetch the carriage

SOURIS:	Je suis un cheval ! Je suis un cheval !
BONNE FÉE:	Amuse-toi au bal, Cendrillon … mais à minuit, il faut partir !

CENDRILLON steps into carriage. All three go back and forth around stage a few times

Scene 2

Le Palais de Versailles

(Optional background music fading out as carriage stops)

SOURIS 1:	Voici le Palais de Versailles !
CENDRILLON:	C'est magnifique !

CENDRILLON steps out of the carriage and enters the ballroom shyly. Meanwhile both the SŒURS are talking to the PRINCE

SŒUR 1:	J'adore ton palais.
SŒUR 2:	Tu gagnes combien ?
PRINCE:	Plus que vous. *(They both turn away in a huff, leaving CENDRILLON in the PRINCE's view. He is instantly smitten with CENDRILLON of course!)*
PRINCE:	T'es belle.
CENDRILLON:	T'es beau. *(They do French greeting, kissing on both cheeks)*
PRINCE:	Tu veux danser ?
CENDRILLON:	Oui, je veux bien.

Play music and fade out (optional). They dance and all guests admire them. SŒURS dance together. SOURIS look on too, giggling excitedly

SOURIS 1:	C'est l'amour ?
SOURIS 2:	Oui, c'est l'amour. *(They make kissing sounds)*

Clock strikes midnight

CENDRILLON:	Minuit déjà !

CENDRILLON runs off, leaving a shoe which PRINCE picks up, admires, then pauses and sniffs, pulls a face

PRINCE:	Ta chaussure ... c'est jolie ... *(sniffs)* ça pue ... le fromage !

Scene 3

Cendrillon's house

CENDRILLON, changed back to rags, comes on stage, sits by fire, sobbing. SOURIS by her feet. SŒURS arrive stomping on again

SŒUR 1:	Pauvre Cendrillon.
SŒUR 2:	Le bal, c'était magnifique.
SŒUR 1:	Le Prince, il était charmant.
PRINCE:	*(Knocks)* Toc, toc, toc.
LES SŒURS:	*(SŒURS hear knock and look surprised)* C'est le Prince ! *(Gasp)*

PRINCE:	*(Holding the shoe out to one of the SŒURS)* C'est ta chaussure ?
SŒUR 1:	C'est trop petit. *(Looks cross and gives it back)*
PRINCE:	*(To other SŒUR)* C'est ta chaussure ?
SŒUR 2:	C'est trop grand.
PRINCE:	*(To CENDRILLON)* Tu veux essayer ?
CENDRILLON:	Oui, je veux bien.
SOURIS:	C'est bon ! *(Shoe fits)*
PRINCE:	Marie-moi !

SOURIS throw veil over CENDRILLON's head

CENDRILLON:	Oui ! Bonne idée !

PRINCE and CENDRILLON look happy and pose as if for a wedding photo. BONNE FÉE arrives

BONNE FÉE:	*(Knocks)* Toc, toc, toc.
SŒUR 1:	*(Very crossly)* Qui est là ? *(Opens door and recognises BONNE FÉE)*
SŒUR 2:	*(Very crossly)* Toi encore ?! *(SŒURS stick tongues out at her)*
BONNE FÉE:	Maintenant **vous** allez travailler ! Allez hop ! *(Zaps them with wand and they are now hard-working. Other characters all stand in a line with arms crossed watching them work)*
SŒURS:	Au travail ! *(They sweep and dust, then polish the other characters' shoes as they say left and right)*
SOURIS 1:	Gauche. *(All put left foot forward to be cleaned)*
SOURIS 2:	Droite. *(All put right foot forward to be cleaned)*

SOURIS 1 counts very quietly under breath to three so that all in the line-up can say in unison

TOUS:	Génial ! *(They make a triumphant gesture)*

Everyone enters stage and takes a bow

FIN

La Petite Poule Rousse

La Petite Poule Rousse

A simple version of a traditional story with the animals' characters brought out by their humorous excuses for not helping the hen.

Theme	
Animals and actions. Food. Table manners	
Language focus	
Simple phrases in present tense. Verbs with 'je'. Everyday language useful for mealtimes.	
Personnages	
Poule (La Petite Poule Rousse)	Little Red Hen (works hard and would like the animals to help)
Coq	Cockerel (crows in the morning to wake everyone up)
Chat	Cat (lazy)
Rat	Rat (lazy and crafty)
Cochon	Pig (lazy, hungry, dirty!)
Mouton	Sheep (lazy)
Canard	Duck (lazy and noisy)
Cheval	Horse (lazy and noisy)
Chien	Dog (playful but lazy)
Vache	Cow (lazy)
Poussins	Chicks (little to say, only present near the end)
Costumes and props	
Animal hoods or masks. Broom. Photo of corn growing tall. Cardboard cupboard with door. Sack of corn, toy cheese or cardboard cheese. Toy sheep or cardboard cut-outs. Sign "30 minutes plus tard". Clock. Real or toy loaf of bread.	
Staging	
Have a table ready for La Petite Poule and her family to sit around for the meal. Pupil holds up photos of various stages of production of bread or consider having a slide show of corn growing, bread baking and other stages of the process if possible, projected on a screen behind the action.	

Scene 1

Farmyard scene

POULE (Hen) sweeps the floor, other animals asleep, COQ (Cockerel) announces morning

COQ:	Cocorico, cocorico.
POULE:	*(To each animal)* Réveille-toi.
EACH ANIMAL IN TURN:	
	Chut, je dors.

POULE sings 'Frère Jacques' to herself gradually getting louder and carries on sweeping, she shouts as she gets to 'Dormez-vous' and jumps at the end for 'Ding dang dong'

TOUS LES ANIMAUX:	Oh là là !

Animals wake up, hands over ears, then go grumpily to sit down at table

COCHON:	Je voudrais mon petit-déjeuner ! *(Pounds fists on table)*
MOUTON:	Je voudrais des céréales.
CHAT:	Oui ... avec du lait. *(Looks hopefully at VACHE (Cow), who shakes her head)*
VACHE:	Je voudrais un croissant.
CANARD:	Ou un pain au chocolat ... mmm, j'adore ça !
POULE:	Désolée, il n'y a rien ! *(Shows them empty cupboard, all animals look cross)*
RAT:	Qu'est-ce qu'on fait ?
POULE:	Il faut travailler !
TOUS LES ANIMAUX:	Travailler ?!
POULE:	Oui. D'abord, je vais semer les graines. *(Looks at all the animals)* Qui veut m'aider ? Monsieur chat, tu veux m'aider ?
CHAT:	Euh ... *(pretends to think)* non.
POULE:	Monsieur cochon ?
COCHON:	Euh ... non.
POULE:	Monsieur rat ?
RAT:	Euh ... non.
POULE:	Monsieur mouton ?

MOUTON:	Beeeeee ... non.

She looks at each of the rest and they all shake their heads in turn and say 'Non'. POULE mimes sowing the seeds, then goes to bed, as do all other animals. COQ crows for the next day

COQ:	Cocorico !

Pupil brings on photograph of field of corn grown tall. POULE wakes, looks pleased and rubs hands with glee

POULE:	Aujourd'hui, je vais couper le blé. Qui veut m'aider ? *(She looks hopefully at the animals, but they each have an excuse)*
COCHON:	Pas moi. Je me lave. *(Washes face, others look surprised!)*
CANARD:	Pas moi, je chante. *(Sings badly)* Meunier, tu dors ? Ton moulin, ton moulin, va trop vite ... .
TOUS LES ANIMAUX:	Chut !
POULE:	Et toi ?
CHEVAL:	Non, je danse. *(Danses with VACHE who looks surprised)*
CHAT:	Non, je lis. *(Pretends to read, others impressed, nod)*
RAT:	Non, je prie. *(Mimes praying, others look amazed, then cross themselves)*

POULE looks disappointed, but cuts the corn by herself and starts to look tired. Tries to pick up a large bag of corn but it's too heavy for her

POULE:	Qui veut m'aider ?
CHEVAL:	Pas moi, je dors. *(Snores like a horse! Yawns and pretends to sleep with head on one side)*
COCHON:	Pas moi, je cours. *(Runs on spot)*
VACHE:	Pas moi, je parle, blah, blah, blah. *(Talks to CANARD)*
CHIEN:	Pas moi, je joue avec le mouton. *(Jumps around MOUTON and tries to get her to play but she isn't interested)*
MOUTON:	Beeeeee, beeeeee.
CANARD:	*(Pictures of sheep or toy sheep to be held up)* Pas moi, je compte les moutons ! 1, 2, 3, 4 ... .

CANARD counts sheep/toy sheep, then MOUTON runs to end of line of sheep to confuse CANARD

RAT:	Pas moi, je cherche du fromage ! *(Sniffs about for cheese. Someone from the wings holds out a piece of cheese and he runs after it then comes back pleased)*
CHAT:	Pas moi, je chasse les rats ! *(Paws at RAT with claws out, RAT runs off and hides with cheese)*

POULE grinds the corn, looking tired

POULE:	Je vais faire la pâte. Qui veut m'aider ?
TOUS LES ANIMAUX:	Moi, non ... non ... non ... . *(All animals one after the other)*

POULE makes the dough and puts the bread in the oven to bake. Someone holds up sign saying '30 minutes plus tard' or winds on the hands of a clock. POULE brings out a lovely fresh loaf

POULE:	Ça sent très bon.
COCHON:	Mmm, ça sent bon. J'ai faim.

Each animal goes to the POULE in turn and asks for bread

CHIEN:	Je peux avoir du pain s'il vous plait ?
POULE:	*(Thinks for a moment)* Non, c'est pour les poussins.

VACHE and all the others follow on with same request, ending with RAT

RAT:	Je peux ... ? *(Before he can even start to speak, POULE interrupts)*
POULE:	Non ! Allez les poussins ... à table.

POUSSINS come in and share the bread

POULE:	Tu veux du pain ?
POUSSINS:	Merci maman ... tu veux du pain ? *(Each POUSSIN offers bread to the next one. Other animals look cross and hungry)*
POUSSINS:	Mmm, c'est délicieux ! *(Rub tummies with satisfaction)*
POULE:	Vous allez travailler maintenant ? *(All animals nod their heads in shame)* Alors, semez les graines. *(She gives them seeds, which they scatter)* Coupez le blé. *(They cut corn. They start to yawn but POULE makes them carry on)* Continuez !

They grind the corn, make the dough, put bread in the oven and take it out – clock and/or sign to indicate 30 minutes passing as before

POULE: Et voilà !

TOUS: Si on travaille bien, on mange du pain ! *(They all look proud of their bread)*

Everyone enters on stage and takes a bow

Pauvre Papa Noël

Pauvre Papa Noël

A simple Christmas play where Father Christmas has to contend with uncooperative reindeer and not very helpful elves. Fortunately, the Fairy from the Christmas tree is on hand with a bit of magic to help him out.

Theme	
Making excuses	
Language focus	
Weather. Time and dates. Illnesses. Countries. Presents	
Personnages	
Papa Noël	Father Christmas (big role, lots of lines)
Rudolphe	Rudolf the Red-nosed reindeer
Elfe 1	Elf 1
Elfe 2 (male)	Elf 2
Fille	Girl
Rennes x 5	5 Reindeer
Fée	Fairy (from top of Christmas tree)
Costumes and props	
Christmas costumes for Father Christmas and elves. Fairy dress and wings. Antler headdresses, red nose. Sack and presents (teddy, bunny, crayons). Letters with countries in large writing. Letter for girl to read. Crutches. Cardboard sledge. Christmas tree or cardboard cut-out of one. Date sign with 'le 25 décembre' on it.	
Staging	
Father Christmas' house. There should be a Christmas tree to one side of the stage near the back. Chair for the girl to sit on on the other side of the stage near the back. Room also needed on stage for Father Christmas to walk to see reindeer. There could be a chair for the fairy to stand on so she looks like she is on the tree.	

Scene 1

Papa Noël's house

FILLE (Girl) on stage in background to the side, ELFES (Elves) and PAPA NOËL (Father Christmas) centre. Christmas tree to other side with FÉE (Fairy) unmoving on top

ELFE 1:	Papa Noël, réveille-toi. Les lettres sont arrivées !
PAPA NOËL:	*(Very grumpy)* Déjà ! Quelle est la date aujourd'hui ?
ELFE 1:	C'est le vingt-quatre décembre !
PAPA NOËL:	Le vingt-quatre décembre ! Ho, ho, ho, oh là là ! Je commence *(Very grumpy; picks up letters randomly)* Canada ... Australie ... Japon *(discards these)* ... France ! *(Opens a letter)*
FILLE:	Cher Papa Noël, *(Starts reading aloud her version of the letter as she writes it. PAPA NOËL reads his version of the letter as she writes it)* Comment allez–vous ? J'ai hâte d'être à Noël ! Je voudrais un nounours pour ma soeur, un lapin pour mon frère et des crayons pour moi s'il vous plait.

FILLE seals and posts letter then goes off stage quietly

PAPA NOËL:	C'est sympa, cette lettre. Alors, un nounours, un lapin et des crayons. Voilà ! *(Puts items in sack)* Rudolphe ... où es-tu ?

RUDOLPHE (Rudolf) limps in on crutches

RUDOLPHE:	*(Crossly)* Oui.
PAPA NOËL:	Il est neuf heures trente, prépare le traineau !
RUDOLPHE:	Ah, non ... . J'ai mal à la jambe.
PAPA NOËL:	Zut ! Qu'est-ce qu'on va faire ?
ELFE 2:	Dépêchez-vous Papa Noël, il est presque dix heures.
PAPA NOËL:	Peux-tu m'aider ?
ELFE 2:	Moi ? Désolé, j'ai mal à la tête. *(Sits by the fire)*
PAPA NOËL:	Mal à la jambe ... mal à la tête. *(Mutters grumpily to himself whilst preparing sack)* Et maintenant il neige ! *(Opens door, sees snow and stomps down the street with his sack to find RENNES (Reindeer)*

PAPA NOËL:	Rennes ! *(Calls RENNES to him, they rush over excitedly)*
RENNE 1:	Bonjour Papa Noël ... où sont les pizzas ?
TOUS LES RENNES:	J'ai faim, j'ai faim.
PAPA NOËL:	Pizzas ? Non ! Il faut nous préparer ... demain c'est Noël !
RENNE 1:	J'ai mal à l'oreille.
PAPA NOËL:	*(Muttering crossly)* Oh, là là, mal à l'oreille ? *(To all the other RENNES)* Vous voulez m'aider ?
RENNE 2:	Non, il fait trop froid.
RENNE 3:	Non, j'ai mal à la gorge.
RENNE 4:	Non, je n'aime pas la neige.
RENNE 5:	Non, je n'aime pas les enfants !

PAPA NOËL goes sadly back down the street to home, sits by the fire with ELFES and looks weary

PAPA NOËL:	Qu'est-ce qu'on va faire ? *(ELFES looks sympathetic)*

FÉE climbs down quietly from tree, creeps behind PAPA NOËL and ELFES and knocks on the door

FÉE:	*(Knocks)* Toc, toc, toc !

PAPA NOËL opens the door grumpily, then pleased to see FÉE

PAPA NOËL:	Ah, bonjour. *(Kisses on each cheek)*
ELFE 2:	Elle est belle ! *(To audience; acts like he really likes her!)*
FÉE:	Arrêtez ! *(To ELFE 2, pushes him lightly away, good humouredly)*
	Papa Noël, les enfants attendent leurs cadeaux. Qu'est-ce qui se passe ?
PAPA NOËL:	Les Rennes sont tous malades ... mal à la jambe ... mal à l'oreille ... .

Freeze-frame of all reindeer, including RUDOLPHE, looking cold, ill, etc

FÉE:	Il faut juste un peu de magie ! Allez hop ! *(She zaps them and they jump up)*
TOUS LES RENNES:	Au travail ! *(They line up in front of FÉE and salute her, then get busy, they march off stage, but RUDOLPHE goes in wrong direction, they call him back)*

TOUS LES RENNES:	Rudolphe ! *(He runs back and joins on their line. They bring sledge on for PAPA NOËL)*
RUDOLPHE:	Voilà !
PAPA NOËL:	Merci beaucoup ! *(Off he goes with bag, dropping presents at houses)*

Pupil comes on with a 'le 25 décembre' date sign. FILLE wakes up next day and finds her presents, excitedly grabbing pencils

FILLE:	Les crayons … . Merci Papa Noël !

PAPA NOËL gives her a cheery wave and bows

Everyone comes back on stage and takes a bow

Fun French Fairy Tale Plays
23

Boucle d'Or

Boucle d'Or

Goldilocks with a twist. Additional characters include a giant and Red Riding Hood, who is a good friend of Goldilocks. The naughty side of Goldilocks is brought out in this version and the inclusion of the giant gives a further comic element.

Theme	
Food	
Language focus	
Useful everyday phrases for preparing and eating food. A few simple phrases in the future and past tense.	
Personnages	
Boucle d'Or	Goldilocks
Sœur	Goldilocks' sister (optional character)
Maman	Mum
Papa Ours	Daddy Bear
Maman Ours	Mummy Bear
Bébé Ours	Baby Bear
Souris x 2	2 mice (optional characters)
Chaperon Rouge	Red Riding Hood
Géant	Giant
Grand-mère	Grandma
Lulu (Chien)	Grandma's dog (optional character)
Forestier	Woodcutter (optional character)
Costumes and props	
Bear hoods, costumes. Honey pot, milk, sugar, basket of fruit and cakes. Cooking pot, three bowls. Cushion and picnic blanket. (Cut-outs of trees – in an ideal world!) Teddy Bears' picnic music.	
Staging	
There are two scenes to this play. One side of the stage could have the scene inside the Three Bears' house, with a table indicating a kitchen. The rest of the stage could be left clear for movement through the forest and the final picnic scene. Trees or any greenery would make a good addition to the forest scenes.	

Scene 1

At Boucle d'Or's (Goldilocks') house

BOUCLE D'OR on stage admiring herself and flicking her hair; MAMAN (Mum) and SŒUR (sister) on stage too

BOUCLE D'OR:	Je suis <u>si</u> belle !
	Maman, j'ai faim ! Qu'est-ce qu'on mange ?
MAMAN:	Des pommes de terre, des petits pois, des carottes et des champignons. Mmmm, c'est très bon ! *(Looks enthusiastic!)*
BOUCLE D'OR:	Oui, c'est très bon ... *(as an aside to the audience only)* pour la santé !
SŒUR:	*(In a goody-two-shoes voice)* Merci Maman, moi, j'adore les légumes. *(MAMAN pleased with her)*
BOUCLE D'OR:	*(In a huff)* Je fais une promenade.
SŒUR:	Je peux venir ?
BOUCLE D'OR:	Non. *(Goes off skipping and singing in the woods, then off stage)* Alouette, gentille alouette, alouette je te plumerai ... .

Scene 2

Trois Ours' house

BÉBÉ OURS:	Bonjour Maman ! On peut faire la cuisine ensemble ?
MAMAN OURS:	Oui, oui. Je vais faire de la soupe.
BÉBÉ OURS:	De la soupe ? À l'oignon. *(Looks disappointed ... then cross)*
MAMAN OURS:	Non, non ... de la soupe au miel. *(Holds up large honey pot)*
BÉBÉ OURS:	Mmm ! Délicieux ! Qu'est-ce qu'on met dans la soupe ?

BÉBÉ OURS (Baby Bear) repeats each item as MAMAN OURS (Mummy Bear) adds them to the pot, then stirs.

MAMAN OURS:	Du lait.
BÉBÉ OURS:	Du lait.
MAMAN OURS:	Du sucre.

BÉBÉ OURS:	Du sucre.
MAMAN OURS:	Et du miel.
BÉBÉ OURS:	Et du miel.

PAPA OURS (Daddy Bear) arrives

PAPA OURS:	Bonjour Bébé. *(Kisses BÉBÉ OURS on top of head)* Bonjour cherie. *(Kisses MAMAN OURS on each cheek as she is pouring three bowls of soup)* Mmm, ça sent bon ! *(Tries to taste soup, but MAMAN OURS stops him by lightly smacking his hand)*
MAMAN OURS:	Non, il faut attendre. On va se promener.

TROIS OURS go off for a walk then off stage. SOURIS (Mice) come out of hiding

SOURIS 1:	Mmm, la soupe au miel. Ça sent bon. J'ai très faim.
SOURIS 2:	On peut ? Oh non, je n'ose pas !

Scene 3

In the woods
BOUCLE D'OR walks back on across the stage

BOUCLE D'OR:	*(Sings last part of Alouette)* Je te plumerai le bec, Je te plumerai le bec, Et le bec, et le bec, Alouette, alouette.

BOUCLE D'OR starts to feel nervous, looks all around her and walks backwards into CHAPERON ROUGE (Red Riding Hood)

CHAPERON ROUGE:	*(Dancing and singing)* Sur le pont d'Avignon. *(Bumps into BOUCLE D'OR. Both girls jump and look scared, then are pleased to see each other)*
CHAPERON ROUGE:	Boucle d'Or !
BOUCLE D'OR:	Chaperon Rouge ! *(French greeting – four kisses on cheeks)* Où vas-tu ?
CHAPERON ROUGE:	Je vais chez ma grand-mère. On va faire un pique-nique.

BOUCLE D'OR:	Qu'est-ce qu'il y a dans ton panier ?
CHAPERON ROUGE:	Des pommes, de la limonade et des gâteaux.
BOUCLE D'OR:	Mmm. Ça sent bon, je peux goûter ?
CHAPERON ROUGE:	Non, c'est pour ma grand-mère ! *(CHAPERON ROUGE pulls basket away crossly and goes off)*

Scene 4

In the woods
GÉANT (Giant) arrives taking big heavy steps, then sniffs; BOUCLE D'OR, frightened, tries to hide

GÉANT:	Ho, hé, ho hum … *(sniffs)* je sens un anglais.
BOUCLE D'OR:	*(Indignantly)* Non, une anglaise !
GÉANT:	J'ai faim. Je vais te manger.

GÉANT starts to move towards BOUCLE D'OR, she faces up to him and steps forward

BOUCLE D'OR:	Va manger des carottes. *(GÉANT steps back as she steps forward)*
GÉANT:	Des carottes ! Je ne suis pas végétarien ! Je suis français ! *(Holds hand over heart in honour pose, facing the audience)*
	Je veux manger du boeuf ou des saucisses, ou des petites filles ! *(Steps forward again towards BOUCLE D'OR and rubs his tummy. She steps back)*

BOUCLE D'OR gasps crossly, sticks her tongue out and scares GÉANT. He stomps off muttering. BOUCLE D'OR runs to Trois Ours' house, gingerly opens door and sees bowls on table

Scene 5

Trois Ours' house
BOUCLE D'OR is on stage. SOURIS are hiding to one side

BOUCLE D'OR:	Mmm, qu'est-ce que c'est ? De la soupe ? Au miel ? *(She tries the three bowls)*
	C'est trop froid … . *(Short pause)*
	C'est trop chaud … . *(Short pause)*
	C'est parfait ! Je vais tout manger. *(Eats up smallest bowl)*
	Je suis fatiguée. *(Yawns and lies down on a cushion)*

TROIS OURS return but SOURIS don't see them at first

SOURIS 1:	Elle dort ?
SOURIS 2:	Oui, on mange ! *(They eat from the bowls of MAMAN OURS and PAPA OURS, but don't finish them)* Au secours ! *(SOURIS see OURS, look scared and hide)*

Scene 6

TROIS OURS look at soup bowls

MAMAN OURS:	Qui a goûté ma soupe ?
PAPA OURS:	Qui a goûté ma soupe ?
BÉBÉ OURS:	*(Cries)* Qui a goûté ma soupe, et l'a toute mangée ?

MAMAN OURS and PAPA OURS comfort BÉBÉ OURS patting him/her on the head

MAMAN OURS:	Mon bébé, ne t'inquiète-pas ! On fera encore de la soupe … .

BÉBÉ OURS spots BOUCLE D'OR asleep

BÉBÉ OURS:	Regarde ! Qui es-tu ?
MAMAN OURS:	Qui es-tu ?
PAPA OURS:	Qui es-tu ?
MAMAN OURS:	As tu goûté ma soupe ?
PAPA OURS:	As-tu goûté ma soupe ?
BÉBÉ OURS:	As-tu mangé ma soupe ?

BOUCLE D'OR wakes up and looks scared

BOUCLE D'OR:	Oui … je suis désolée … j'ai peur. Au secours !

OURS roar at her one after the other and lean over her with their claws out. They need to freeze-frame this pose and hold it for a few minutes. CHAPERON ROUGE arrives with GRAND-MÈRE (Grandma), FORESTIER (Woodcutter), SŒUR and LULU (a dog)

CHAPERON ROUGE:	On mange ici grand-mère ? *(Spreads the picnic cloth on ground)*

GRAND-MÈRE:	Oui, c'est très bien ici.
FORESTIER:	C'est très beau. J'ai faim. Qu'est-ce qu'on mange ?
LULU:	Wouf! Wouf ! *(Tries to get them to see the OURS)*
GRAND-MÈRE:	Arrête, Lulu ! Assieds-toi !
GRAND-MÈRE:	Oh, là là, regarde – c'est Boucle d'Or ! *(GRAND-MÈRE is shocked to see BOUCLE D'OR being threatened by all TROIS OURS – all still in frozen pose)*
FORESTIER:	Non, non, non ! Ne la tuez pas !
SŒUR:	Personne ne fait de mal à ma soeur ! *(SŒUR faces up to TROIS OURS)*
CHAPERON ROUGE:	Asseyez-vous. On va faire le pique-nique des nounours. *(Takes each bear by the hand and sits them down gently. Gets out cakes, lemonade, and honey)*
CHAPERON ROUGE:	Voilà ! Des gâteaux, de la limonade, du miel.
LULU:	Et du vin rouge ! *(Passes red wine to GRAND-MÈRE who immediately takes a swig)*
GRAND-MÈRE:	C'est très bon ... hic ! *(Getting tipsy!)*
LES TROIS OURS:	Mmm, c'est bon.

They all sit down and look happy, teddy bears' picnic music plays in background, 3 OURS, FORESTIER, LULU and GRAND-MÈRE eat and gradually drift off to sleep, GRAND-MÈRE a bit tipsy

CHAPERON ROUGE:	Viens ! *(The girls creep away and high five each other over the top of the group as they go)*

Everyone comes back on stage and takes a bow

Rapunzel et la tour Eiffel

Rapunzel et la tour Eiffel

Imagine if Rapunzel lived at the top of, not just any old tower, but the Eiffel Tower. Well, that's where our heroine finds herself, but she is not very happy. If only she had some friends to keep her company on her birthday ... . As luck would have it, some well-loved characters from other stories have just arrived in Paris for their holiday.

Theme	
Friends. Appearance and personality	
Language focus	
Adjectives for describing people. Use of '*être*' in the present tense. Comparative adjectives. A few phrases in the future tense using '*aller*'.	
Personnages	
Rapunzel	Stuck in the Eiffel Tower for 16 years, lonely, needs friends (big role)
Alice	From Wonderland (along with White Rabbit), usually nice, sometimes a bit unkind
Lapin Blanc	White Rabbit – Energetic, sporty, impatient, in a hurry (some tricky lines)
Prince Charmant	Prince Charming – Much too charming, a bit full of himself, looking for a princess!
Cendrillon	Cinderella – Hard-working, polite and a good friend (managable lines)
Sorcière / Maman	Witch/Mum – Evil witch who pretends to be Rapunzel's Mum. Has kept Rapunzel locked up for 16 years in the Eiffel Tower (small role, but a few tricky lines)
Rumplestiltskin	Talkative and short! (a few tricky lines)
Costumes and props	
Window for Rapunzel, broom, long-haired wig. Cardboard cut-out of an Eiffel Tower about as tall as the pupils. Large pictures of lift, doors and stairs. Sign with 'Défense d'entrer. En panne. Depuis seize ans'. Rabbit ears, white fur, pocket watch, blue dress (for Alice) and other appropriate costumes. Pieces of paper and pencil. Cardboard cut-out of taxi. Ring box. Potion bottle (optional). Model cakes – (one green, one brown), sugar cubes, butter in packet, chocolate eggs, bowl.	
Staging	
Stage needs to be divided into two halves if possible with Rapunzel in her tower on one side and the other half of the stage for the scenes outside the Eiffel Tower. Window needs to be big enough for Rapunzel to lean out of and firmly positioned. There should be a sign about the broken lift at the bottom of the tower.	

Scene 1

Paris
RAPUNZEL leaning out of her window of the Eiffel Tower, other characters come on and introduce themselves, without even noticing her

RAPUNZEL:	Je m'appelle Rapunzel. *(Waves from her window)*
CENDRILLON:	Je m'appelle Cendrillon. *(Leans on her broom)*
ALICE:	Je m'appelle Alice. *(Curtsies)*
RUMPLESTILTSKIN:	Je m'appelle Rumplestiltskin. *(Waves to audience)*
PRINCE:	Je suis le Prince Charmant. *(Takes off hat and bows extravagantly)*

LAPIN BLANC (White Rabbit) runs on

LAPIN BLANC:	*(Panting)* Je suis le lapin blanc, et je suis en retard. *(Runs off, looking at watch)*
TOUS:	Nous sommes à Paris en vacances !

They pose, LAPIN BLANC runs back on and takes a photo quickly, they all leave quietly, SORCIÈRE (Witch) comes on but they don't see her

SORCIÈRE:	Et moi, je suis la sorcière. *(Sweeps her cloak around her dramatically. Only RAPUNZEL notices her)*
RAPUNZEL:	Maman ! *(Waves to SORCIÈRE)*
SORCIÈRE:	*(Waves back pretending to be nice and says as an aside to the audience and laughs)* Je ne suis pas sa maman.

Scene 2

Rapunzel's room in the Eiffel Tower
RAPUNZEL sitting by window brushing hair

RAPUNZEL:	Aujourd'hui c'est mon anniversaire. J'ai seize ans ... *(pauses)* mais je suis toute seule. *(Looks sad)* J'ai une idée ! *(Suddenly looks pleased as she has the idea of writing a list of qualities she wants in a friend. Talks as she writes on several pieces of paper)*

RAPUNZEL:	Recherche : ami(e) pour jeune fille ... qui habite ... non, qui est <u>prisonnière</u> à la tour Eiffel.
	Doit être ... *(pauses to think)* sympa ... charmant ... fort ... bavard ... . Et ? Sportif, oui, sportif. *(Picks up notes)*
SORCIÈRE:	Rapunzel ! *(Calls out, then comes in holding cake)*

RAPUNZEL hides notes behind back, then throws them out of the window rather than let SORCIÈRE see them

SORCIÈRE:	Joyeux anniversaire, Rapunzel. *(Kisses on both cheeks, gives birthday cake)*
RAPUNZEL:	Merci ... . Un gâteau pour moi ! *(She is pleased at first, then realises it is green – says disgustedly)* Beurk ... c'est un gâteau à la salade ?!
SORCIÈRE:	Oui, c'est très bien pour ... pour ... pour les cheveux !
RAPUNZEL:	Les cheveux ! *(Indignantly)* J'ai les cheveux très longs, maman !

RAPUNZEL looks out of window and lets hair fall out

SORCIÈRE:	Je sais ! Je vais au marché, au revoir.

SORCIÈRE starts to climb down hair, RAPUNZEL groans as she pulls on her hair, then SORCIÈRE sticks head back through window, giving RAPUNZEL a fright

SORCIÈRE:	Ne sors pas Rapunzel ... c'est dangereux !

SORCIÈRE goes off stage

RAPUNZEL:	Dangereux ! C'est ridicule. Je vais faire un gâteau au chocolat. *(RAPUNZEL drops green cake in bin. Crossly gets bowl and puts ingredients in: sugar cubes, butter in packet, chocolate eggs in foil!)*
	Sucre, beurre, oeufs.

Scene 3

Outside 'la tour Eiffel'
The other characters arrive by taxi and gather as tourists, taking photos and admiring the tower

PRINCE:	Voici la tour Eiffel !

ALICE:	C'est magnifique !
RUMPLESTILTSKIN:	C'est très haut ... . Trois cent mètres ... oh là là !
LAPIN BLANC:	On va monter ?
RUMPLESTILTSKIN:	Oui ... euh ... on prend l'ascenseur ? *(Points to picture of lift)*

Goes over to lift and takes no entry sign off, then reads notice out loud

RUMPLESTILTSKIN:	Défense d'entrer. En panne ... depuis seize ans ! Zut !

All characters look shocked and look at each other in disbelief

TOUS:	Seize ans. Zut !

CENDRILLON notices pieces of paper on floor

CENDRILLON:	Qu'est-ce que c'est? *(Picks them up and starts to read them)*
	Jeune fille ... seize ans ... cherche des amis ... .
	Prisonnière à la tour Eiffel.
TOUS:	Prisonnière ? *(All characters gasp and look up ... CENDRILLON reads on)*
CENDRILLON:	... Préfère des amis ... sympa ... *(pauses)* sympa ? Je suis sympa ! *(She looks pleased. RUMPLESTILTSKIN, LAPIN BLANC and PRINCE agree with a nod, but ALICE has other ideas!)*
ALICE:	Non ! Moi, je suis sympa ! *(Takes papers from CENDRILLON, who then sadly picks up a broom and starts sweeping. Meanwhile ALICE continues reading notes)*
	Sportif ... .
LAPIN BLANC:	Je suis sportif. *(He runs on the spot and does press-ups or he picks up taxi and runs off with it! ALICE is impressed)*
ALICE:	*(Still reading notes)* Charmant ... .
PRINCE:	Je suis très charmant. *(Bows to CENDRILLON, takes broom from her and starts sweeping. CENDRILLON looks dreamily at him, like she might fall in love with him!)*
CENDRILLON:	Il est sympa !

LAPIN BLANC:	C'est ridicule ! *(CENDRILLON swoons over PRINCE; LAPIN BLANC tuts impatiently)*
ALICE:	*(Continues reading notes)* Bavard … .
RUMPLESTILTSKIN:	Je suis bavard ! Blah, blah, blah, blah … . *(Others cover their ears)*
ALICE:	*(Still reading)* Et fort.
PRINCE:	Je suis fort ! *(He flexes his muscles, then picks up 'la tour Eiffel'. CENDRILLON is impressed)*

RAPUNZEL stumbles across her moving floor, then yells out the window to him

RAPUNZEL:	Arrêtez ! *(PRINCE puts 'la tour Eiffel' down and LAPIN BLANC talks crossly to him)*
LAPIN BLANC:	*(Impatiently taps watch)* Excusez-moi … . Je suis en retard. On va monter ou non ?
TOUS:	*(Excitedly because they want to meet RAPUNZEL)* Oui, on va voir Rapunzel !
LAPIN BLANC:	On prend l'escalier ? *(Limbers up ready to climb upstairs)*
TOUS:	Oui … *(keen at first, then look up at height of tower and change minds)* euh … non !

They all move to face audience in a line to give their excuses

RUMPLESTILTSKIN:	Moi, je suis trop petit.
ALICE:	Moi aussi. Je suis trop petite. Non, trop grande … trop petite … trop grande … . *(Makes herself small, big, small, big as in Wonderland story. She could pretend to swig from a potion bottle between each phrase)*
LAPIN BLANC:	C'est ridicule ! On y va … ! *(He starts to run upstairs)* 1, 2, 3, 4, 5, 6, 7, 8, 9, 10 … *(runs and puffs)* 20 … *(puffs some more)* 50 … oh, là, là … c'est trop … . *(Sits exhausted, ALICE comforts him)*
PRINCE:	Permettez-moi. *(Shouts to RAPUNZEL)* Rapunzel … laisse tomber tes cheveux !

Hair comes falling down … PRINCE climbs up, then goes down on one knee and opens ring box

PRINCE:	Rapunzel, marie-moi ?
RAPUNZEL:	Oh, t'es rapide ! Mais non ! *(She is surprised then shakes her head)*

ALICE and CENDRILLON climb up hair next. PRINCE proposes to both

PRINCE:	*(To ALICE)* Marie-moi ?
ALICE:	Euh ... non !
PRINCE:	*(To CENDRILLON)* Marie-moi ?
CENDRILLON:	*(She is tempted)* Peut-être ... . *(ALICE pulls her away)*
ALICE:	Non !

PRINCE looks annoyed but then hears someone climbing up and listens with interest, ready to propose again! RUMPLESTILTSKIN climbs up and PRINCE hastily changes his mind

PRINCE:	Marie ... euh, non ... .

RUMPLESTILTSKIN sees ring box and snatches it off him then throws it over his shoulder. LAPIN BLANC catches box and climbs up then tries to propose to PRINCE CHARMANT!

LAPIN:	Marie-moi ? *(PRINCE looks really annoyed!)*

RAPUNZEL excitedly greets her new friends

ALICE:	Je m'appelle Alice. *(Curtsies and smiles)*
RAPUNZEL:	Enchantée. *(Shakes hands)*
CENDRILLON:	Je m'appelle Cendrillon. *(Curtsies and smiles)*
RAPUNZEL:	Enchantée. *(Shakes hands)*
RUMPLETSTILTSKIN:	Je m'appelle Rumplestiltskin. *(He bows)*
RAPUNZEL:	Enchantée. *(Shakes hands)*
LAPIN BLANC:	Je m'appelle ... *(not sure of own name)* bah, je suis le lapin blanc.
RAPUNZEL:	Enchantée. *(Shakes hands)*

Girls start to make friends

CENDRILLON:	Tes cheveux sont beaux ! *(Admires RAPUNZEL's hair)*
ALICE:	Ta robe est belle. *(Admires dress)*

RAPUNZEL: J'ai des amis ! Je suis très heureuse.

RAPUNZEL links arms with new friends, they go off and find the cake. PRINCE sulks in the corner. LAPIN BLANC and RUMPLESTILTSKIN try to comfort him

RUMPLESTILTSKIN: Blah, blah, blah, blah … . *(Not too loudly)*

All girls come back, bringing cake in

ALICE et CENDRILLON: Mmm, ça sent bon.

PRINCE: À table. On mange. *(PRINCE cheers up at arrival of cake)*

Everyone sits down, RAPUNZEL at window. SORCIÈRE appears outside at the bottom of 'la tour Eiffel', wants to come up

SORCIÈRE: Rapunzel, Rapunzel, laisse tomber tes cheveux. Je veux monter.

RAPUNZEL: C'est maman ! *(RAPUNZEL looks annoyed and lets down her hair impatiently)*

LAPIN BLANC: Non, c'est une sorcière !

RAPUNZEL: Huh … ! *(Gasps as she realises SORCIÈRE isn't her mum)* Ce n'est pas ma mère ?

LAPIN BLANC: Non.

RAPUNZEL: Génial ! *(Very pleased … pauses)* Alors … coupez mes cheveux ! *(Decisively)*

CENDRILLON: Coupez les cheveux ? *(Looks worried and upset)*

PRINCE: Permettez-moi ! *(Flexes his muscles, and poses like a body builder. Mimes scissors with fingers)*

LAPIN BLANC comes up behind him, pulls the wig off RAPUNZEL and lets it fall

LAPIN BLANC: Voilà ! *(PRINCE looks really cross with LAPIN BLANC)*

RAPUNZEL: Mes cheveux !

RAPUNZEL looks down from window. SORCIÈRE falls and hobbles off clutching her bottom

SORCIÈRE: Aie … mon derrière !

RAPUNZEL: Pfiou !

RUMPLESTILTSKIN: Alors le gâteau ! *(Cuts the cake and gives everyone a piece)*

TOUS: Bon anniversaire, Rapunzel, bon anniversaire.

Everyone takes a bow

FIN

Le Chat Botté

Le Chat Botté

A traditional tale given a few twists. In this version, the cat is keen to get his master (Marc) working so that he earns the respect of the King. In fact, Marc ends up deciding he'd have more fun staying with his brothers and Dad than marrying a princess. Also, contrary to the wishes of the King, the Princess is more interested in horses and would love to be a show-jumper … . But don't worry, there is romance in the air for some of the characters!

Theme	
Family	
Language focus	
Adjectives, clothes, opinions. Several traditional French songs.	
Personnages	
Père	Father
Fils 1 Jean	Eldest son
Fils 2 Luc	Second son
Fils 3 Marc	Youngest son (cat calls him Maître and Marc de Carabas)
Cheval	Family horse (hard-working, likes the Princess)
Chat Botté	Puss in Boots (very clever, likes smart clothes, vain. Considers Marc his master, but really he is in charge!)
Roi	King (lives in castle with three daughters, house overrun by mice)
Princesse	Princess, kings eldest daughter (loves horses)
Chat blanc	White cat (female, very beautiful, belongs to Princess, hopeless hunter)
Souris	Mice (live in castle, over-confident and not scared of white cat)
Sœurs x 2	Like sport (and possibly the brothers)
Costumes and props	
Smart clothing for King, Princess and spare smart jacket for Marc. Working clothes for brothers, including T-shirt, shorts, socks, hat for Marc. Spare hat, socks. Cat hoods or masks, and boots, hat, suit. Model or picture of windmill and small beach windmill with sails that you can blow round. Clock with hands that spin round. Horse hood. Mouse hoods or ears and tails. Baskets x 3 and vegetables, fruit, soft toys, especially bunnies. Signs for 'lundi', 'mardi' and 'mercredi'. Plastic wine bottle. Screen with scene of pool and swimmer in it. Sword. Photo of Princess as a show-jumper to be displayed on stage.	
Staging	
The spare clothes need to be on stage in a discreet pile ready for river scene (Scene 6).	

Scene 1

At the family farm

PÈRE (Father), JEAN, LUC and MARC all working together. PÈRE calls/whistles for sons to stop and they gather together

PÈRE:	Mes fils ... je suis vieux.
TOUS:	Ah non, Papa !
PÈRE:	Si ... et je suis fatigué. Vous allez travailler plus à la ferme.
TOUS:	Oui, Papa.
PÈRE:	Jean, voici ... mon moulin. *(Gives him windmill)*
JEAN:	*(Looks pleased)* C'est super ! Merci Papa.
PÈRE:	Luc, voici ... mon cheval.
LUC:	*(Looks pleased)* Il est magnifique. Merci Papa.
PÈRE:	Marc, voici ... mon chat.
MARC:	*(A bit disappointed)* Ton chat ? Merci Papa.
CHAT BOTTÉ:	Miaou.
PÈRE:	Travaillez dur mes fils.
JEAN:	Asseyez-vous Papa. *(Gets PÈRE to sit down)*
TOUS:	Au travail. Au revoir, Papa. *(They limber up enthusiastically and get ready for work)*

Scene 2

Outside

Brothers are discussing and admiring their gifts

MARC:	Toi, tu as le moulin, toi, tu as le cheval ... *(older two look proudly at their gifts)*
	et moi ... j'ai le chat !
CHAT BOTTÉ:	Miaou ! *(Other brothers go; CHAT BOTTÉ (Puss in Boots) nuzzles up to MARC)*
MARC:	Tu es gentil, petit chat. *(Strokes CHAT BOTTÉ)* Mais on sera pauvre ... très pauvre. *(In despair, sobs)*
CHAT BOTTÉ:	Miaou. Écoute-moi.

MARC:	*(Gasps as he hears CHAT BOTTÉ speak)* Oooh ! Tu parles !
CHAT BOTTÉ:	Oui ... travaille dur et tu seras riche !
MARC:	Riche ... impossible !
CHAT BOTTÉ:	Si ! Écoute-moi. D'abord, je voudrais un sac et des bottes.
MARC:	Des bottes ? *(MARC moves off to get them)*
CHAT BOTTÉ:	*(Keeps shouting for more things as MARC searches for them)* Oui, et un chapeau ... une veste ... un pantalon.
MARC:	Voilà.
CHAT BOTTÉ:	Merci. *(Gets dressed, admires himself, arranges hat and smoothes out whiskers)* Ça va très bien. *(To MARC)* Maître, au travail.

Scene 3

In the fields

MARC works hard in the fields all day long, looks tired. Someone holds up a clock with hands whirring round to show the day progressing. MARC starts to walk home with vegetables he has collected, singing as he goes. Suddenly he spots JEAN sleeping beside his windmill, which is going too fast (someone needs to blow the beach windmill quite fast!) MARC stops beside his brother, then sings louder and faster to wake his brother up

MARC:	*(Gentle at first, getting louder)*
	Meunier tu dors? Ton moulin, ton moulin va trop vite.
	Meunier tu dors? Ton moulin, ton moulin va trop fort.
	Ton moulin, ton moulin va trop vite.
	Ton moulin, ton moulin va trop fort. *(Repeat the last two lines singing faster, jumping up and down and shouting)*

Brother JEAN wakes up suddenly and MARC helps him stop the windmill

JEAN:	Merci mon frère.

MARC sees his other brother LUC further on down the road, singing as if drunk. LUC catches hold of MARC and forces MARC to dance with him

LUC:	*(Singing)* Sur le pont d'Avignon,
	On y danse, on y danse
	Sur le pont d'Avignon,
	On y danse tous en rond.

MARC:	*(A bit crossly)* Arrête ! Où est le cheval ?
LUC:	Je ne sais pas ! *(Shrugs, shakes head and holds hands out)*

MARC goes off to find CHEVAL (horse)

LUC:	*(Falls in a sleepy heap on the floor, then hiccups)* Hic !

MARC finds CHEVAL, who looks worried

MARC:	*(To horse)* Voilà ! Comment ça va ?
CHEVAL:	*(In a type of neigh)* Hi, hi, hi. J'ai mal à la tête. *(Holds hands over ears)*
MARC:	Tu parles aussi ! Viens. *(Leads horse home)* Voilà. Repose-toi. *(Lets him rest and eat grass)*

CHAT BOTTÉ returns and sees vegetables, then quickly arranges them in a basket

CHAT BOTTÉ:	*(Seizes basket)* Excellent. Vous avez bien travaillé !
MARC:	Mais, c'est mon dîner !

Scene 4

At the castle

CHAT BOTTÉ goes off with basket of food, singing. Someone holds up sign for 'lundi'. CHAT BOTTÉ arrives at castle and knocks on the door

CHAT BOTTÉ:	Lundi matin, l'empereur, sa femme et le petit Prince sont venus chez moi pour me serrer la pince ... . Toc, toc, toc.
ROI:	Oui ... ah, bonjour ! *(Surprised to see a cat!)*
CHAT BOTTÉ:	Un cadeau de mon maître : Marc de Carabas ! *(Says name of master proudly)*
ROI:	Merci beaucoup. *(Takes basket CHAT BOTTÉ offers)*

Someone holds up sign for 'mardi'. CHAT BOTTÉ goes off and comes back on again quickly with basket of fruit

CHAT BOTTÉ:	*(Singing)* Mardi matin, l'empereur, sa femme et le petit Prince sont venus chez moi pour me serrer la pince ... . *(Knocks at castle door again)* Toc, toc, toc.

ROI:	Oui ... bonjour. *(Pleased to see cat again)*
CHAT BOTTÉ:	Un cadeau de mon maître : Marc de Carabas.
ROI:	Merci beaucoup.

Someone holds up sign for 'mercredi'. CHAT BOTTÉ goes off and on again quickly, with basket of soft toys, so he looks like a good hunter

CHAT BOTTÉ:	*(Singing)* Mercredi matin, l'empereur, sa femme et le petit Prince sont venus chez moi pour me serrer la pince ... . *(Knocks at castle door again)* Toc, toc, toc.
ROI:	Oui, bonjour ... monsieur chat.
CHAT BOTTÉ:	Un cadeau de mon maître : Marc de Carabas.
ROI:	Merci ... votre maître est très généreux. Attendez. *(Invites cat inside, and calls out quietly, becoming louder)* Princesses ... princesses ... princesses !

PRINCESSE (Princess) arrives with SŒURS 1 et 2 (Sisters 1 and 2) and CHAT BLANC (White Cat)

PRINCESSE:	Oui, Papa.
CHAT BLANC:	Miaou ! *(Looks at CHAT BOTTÉ with interest!)*
CHAT BOTTÉ:	Miaou ! *(Makes purring sounds)*
SŒUR 1:	Regarde les chats. *(Nudges SŒUR 2 to look at cats)*
SŒUR 2:	Regarde les souris. *(Nudges SŒUR 1 to look at mice)*

SOURIS (MICE) saunter into room, singing

SOURIS:	Alouette, gentille alouette ... . Alouette je te plumerai.

Then the SOURIS see the CHAT BOTTÉ, gasp and hide behind the chair

SOURIS:	Chut ! C'est le Chat Botté !
PRINCESSE:	*(Beckons CHAT BOTTÉ over)* Monsieur chat ... j'ai un problème : mon chat ne chasse pas les souris !

CHAT BLANC goes over to SOURIS and purrs at them. CHAT BOTTÉ rolls his eyes and shakes his head/ finger at CHAT BLANC

ROI:	J'ai une idée. Vous êtes un très bon chasseur. Restez ici.

CHAT BOTTÉ thinks, nods to ROI (King) and shows his claws to SOURIS who run off stage. He is tempted by offer but hesitates

CHAT BOTTÉ:	Bonne idée ... mais, j'en parle d'abord à mon maître.
ROI:	D'accord. Mes filles, venez ... on va se promener.
PRINCESSES:	*(Saluting their father)* Oui, Papa.

CHAT BOTTÉ runs back to farm – across stage a couple of times; ROI and PRINCESSES walk slowly

Scene 5

At the farm

FRÈRES (the three brothers) and PÈRE are singing and enjoying each other's company

TOUS:	Frère Jacques, Frère Jacques. Dormez–vous ? Dormez–vous ? *(Normal version)*

CHAT BOTTÉ arrives and stops them, pulling MARC away

CHAT BOTTÉ:	Arrête ! Viens vite, le Roi va passer ! *(MARC hastily jumps on horse, and they rush to the river)*

Scene 6

At the river

CHAT BOTTÉ:	Voici la rivière ... . Nage !
MARC:	Nage ?! *(CHAT nods)* Mes vêtements !
CHAT BOTTÉ:	Enlève-les !
MARC:	Enlève-les ?!
CHAT BOTTÉ:	Oui !

MARC goes reluctantly behind screen, chucks spare hat and socks over screen as if he has just taken them off and pretends to swim. Then ROI and PRINCESSES arrive. Eldest admires horse

PRINCESSE:	Regardez le cheval.
SŒUR 1:	Tu aimes faire du cheval ?
PRINCESSE:	Oui, j'adore ça. Et toi ?

SŒUR 1:	Je préfère me promener.
SŒUR 2:	Et moi, j'aime nager ! *(Looks with interest at MARC swimming in water)*
PRINCESSE:	*(To horse, stroking him)* Tu es beau.

CHEVAL neighs

ROI:	Ah, bonjour monsieur chat.
CHAT BOTTÉ:	Bonjour votre Majesté … . *(CHAT BOTTÉ tries to kiss the hand of ROI, but ROI snatches it away)* Voici Marc de Carabas ! *(CHAT BOTTÉ points at MARC swimming. SŒURS giggle and look interested!)*
ROI:	Enchanté, monsieur. *(ROI is delighted to meet MARC who stretches arm around screen to shake hands with him)*
CHAT BOTTÉ:	*(Explains MARC's reluctance to appear)* Il a perdu son t-shirt !
ROI:	Ah, je comprends … voici ma veste. *(ROI gives him his own jacket)*
MARC:	Merci.
ROI:	Merci **à vous** pour tous les cadeaux. Venez au château ! *(They go back to castle)*
SŒUR 2:	Oui, oui, venez manger chez nous. *(They continue walking and arrive at castle)*
SŒUR 1:	Voici le château … entrez !
MARC:	C'est magnifique !
ROI:	Asseyez-vous. *(ROI indicates for MARC to sit, but there is no chair so he kneels)*

CHAT BLANC comes in and stays close to CHAT BOTTÉ, they 'Miaou' at each other

CHAT BLANC:	Comment ça va ?
CHAT BOTTÉ:	Ça va bien merci, et toi ?
CHAT BLANC:	Maintenant, ça va très bien. *(CHAT BLANC snuggles up to him)* Miaou, miaou, miaou.

ROI decides to honour MARC, to his great surprise. He places a crown on MARC's head and touches both shoulders with his sword

ROI:	Voilà. Vous êtes un vrai Prince maintenant !

MARC: *(Looking surprised)* Merci, mais … je préfère habiter avec mes frères.

MARC gives crown back and waves to LUC and JEAN in the distance, CHEVAL on stage too now

ROI: Oh !

PRINCESSE: Vous avez combien de frères ?

MARC: Deux. Et vous ?

PRINCESSE: J'ai deux sœurs. *(Points to SŒURS who wave to LUC and JEAN excitedly)*

SŒURS: Bonjour, bonjour !

PRINCESSE stands by CHEVAL stroking him

PRINCESSE: J'adore ton cheval … . *(CHEVAL nuzzles up to her)*

ROI: Alors vous partez. *(To MARC, who nods)* Et vous ? *(To CHAT BOTTÉ)*

CHAT BOTTÉ: Je préfère rester ici. On va chasser les souris !

CHAT BLANC: Oui, montre-moi comment chasser les souris !

CHAT BOTTÉ beckons CHAT BLANC over and mimes to her how to wait, get claws out and pounce … then she proposes!

CHAT BLANC: Merci … marie-moi ? *(CHAT BOTTÉ who is unsure looks at the other characters questioningly, but they all nod to him)*

TOUS: Dis oui !

CHAT BOTTÉ: Oui. *(They link arms and someone gives them flowers)*

PRINCESSE poses with CHEVAL, wearing a riding hat and rosette. One of the brothers takes a photo of her

ROI: C'est super. Merci pour tout, Marc. *(Shakes MARC's hand)* On fait la fête !

SOURIS 1: On va chanter 'Frère Jacques' maintenant ?

SOURIS 2: Oui, 'Frère Jacques Rock and Roll' !

All cast on stage to sing rock and roll version of Frère Jacques, with hand jive and dancing

FIN

Blanche-Neige et les nains sportifs

Blanche-Neige et les nains sportifs

Snow White on a sporty theme. The traditional story of Snow White is given a twist here with seven sporty dwarves and a golf-mad heroine.

Theme	
Sport and hobbies	
Language focus	
Key phrases for sports, hobbies, activities and household chores. Simple phrases in present, past and future tense with 'aller'.	
Personnages	
Blanche-Neige	Snow White
Miroir	Mirror
Reine	Queen
Dracula (mari de la Reine)	Husband (he seems scary at first, but he has to do what his wife wants!)
Nain 1 nageur	Swimming dwarf
Nain 2 joueur de foot	Football dwarf
Nain 3 danseur	Dancing dwarf
Nain 4 joueur de tennis	Tennis dwarf
Nain 5 gymnaste	Gymnastic dwarf
Nain 6 chanteur	Singing dwarf
Nain 7 dormeur	Sleepy dwarf (comic role)
Vieille Dame	Old lady/Queen
Prince	Prince
Président du club de golf	President of the golf club
Membres du club	Club members (could double up as dwarves)
Costumes and props	
Mirror. Dwarf hats, dark cloak for husband, suitable clothes for all characters. Apple, broom, knitting. Sign with 'Au Club de Golf' on it, toy golf club, golf cup (or crown). Cooking pot and ingredients, plates, table and chairs.	
Staging	
Stage to be set for a simple interior scene for the Queen's room and the inside of the Dwarves' house. A table and chairs are needed for the meal scene.	

Scene 1

Blanche-Neige's (Snow White's) home
REINE (Queen) and MIROIR (Mirror) are on stage

REINE:	Miroir, Miroir, qui est la plus belle du monde ? *(Admires herself in the mirror)*
MIROIR:	Pas vous ! C'est Blanche-Neige !
REINE:	*(Crossly)* Blanche-Neige ! *(Then to MIROIR, hoping for a positive response)* Miroir, Miroir, qui est la meilleure danseuse ? *(Spins round)*
MIROIR:	Pas vous. C'est Blanche-Neige !
REINE:	*(More crossly!)* Blanche-Neige ! Miroir, Miroir, qui est le meilleur joueur de golf ? *(Mimes playing golf)*
MIROIR:	Pas vous. C'est Blanche-Neige.
REINE:	Blanche-Neige ! *(Furious now)* Où est mon mari ? *(Calls out increasingly loud and cross)* Dracula.

DRACULA arrives and sweeps his cloak around himself dramatically looking at the audience

REINE:	On va jouer au golf !
DRACULA:	Oui, ma chérie. *(Goes off with REINE as a dutiful husband)*

Scene 2

At the golf club
BLANCHE-NEIGE plays a winning shot and club members cheer!

TOUS:	Hourrah ! Blanche-Neige a gagné.

PRÉSIDENT DU CLUB DE GOLF (President of the golf club) crowns BLANCHE-NEIGE or gives her a cup

PRÉSIDENT:	Félicitations Blanche-Neige. La championne de golf !
TOUS:	Hourrah, hourrah !

REINE arrives

REINE:	Championne ? Imbécile ! Allez ! *(Waves BLANCHE-NEIGE off the stage)* Et ne revenez plus.

REINE goes off stage, looking pleased to be rid of BLANCHE-NEIGE

Scene 3

In the woods. The Dwarves' cottage is to the side

BLANCHE-NEIGE wanders back on to stage as if walking through the woods, looking worried

BLANCHE-NEIGE: *(To the audience)*

Qu'est-ce que je vais faire ? *(Carries on wandering and finds the cottage)*

Quelle jolie maison ... . *(Knocks on the door)*

Qui est là ? *(Goes in and looks around and touches all the objects eg radio, TV)*

C'est super. Je peux écouter la radio ... jouer du piano ...

regarder la télé. *(Sits down, then leaps up)*

Non, je vais travailler. *(Sweeps the floor, and starts cooking, sings to herself)*

Alouette, gentille alouette.

Alouette, je te plumerai ... .

Le dîner ? Mmm, c'est bon ! *(Puts more ingredients in and stirs pot)*

TOUS LES NAINS (all the dwarves) come home from work

TOUS LES NAINS: *(Singing)* Sur le pont d'Avignon, on y danse, on y danse

Sur le pont d'Avignon, on y danse, tous en rond.

As they get to the cottage and see door open, they are worried and stop abruptly, crashing into each other

TOUS LES NAINS: *(Each one turns round and says to the one behind)*

Oh là là. *(The last one, NAIN 7, does this too, even though there is no one behind him/her)*

They go through the door, see BLANCHE-NEIGE, gasp and look frightened

NAIN 1: Qui êtes-vous ?

BLANCHE-NEIGE: Je suis Blanche-Neige, et vous ?

Each dwarf introduces himself and mimes his or her activity. They all stand in a line facing the audience

NAIN 1: Je suis nageur. *(Mimes swimming)*

BLANCHE-NEIGE: Enchantée ! *(Moves along line kissing each on the forehead, they look pleased but embarrassed!)*

NAIN 2: Je suis joueur de foot. *(Mimes kicking ball)*

BLANCHE-NEIGE: Enchantée !

NAIN 3:	Je suis danseur. *(Mimes dancing)*
BLANCHE-NEIGE:	Enchantée !
NAIN 4:	Je suis joueur de tennis. *(Mimes playing tennis)*
BLANCHE-NEIGE:	Enchantée !
NAIN 5:	Je suis gymnaste. *(Mimes gymnastic moves)*
BLANCHE-NEIGE:	Enchantée !
NAIN 6:	*(Sings)* Je suis chanteur.
BLANCHE-NEIGE:	Enchantée !
NAIN 7:	*(Sleeps)* Je suis dormeur !
BLANCHE-NEIGE:	Enchantée !
NAIN 1:	Quel travail ! *(Looks around at the clean house)*
NAIN 2:	La maison est propre.
NAIN 3:	Mmm, ça sent bon. *(Smells the lovely food cooking in the pot)*
NAIN 4:	J'ai faim !

TOUS LES NAINS try to sit down to eat, looking hopeful, but BLANCHE-NEIGE sends them off

BLANCHE-NEIGE:	Non, il faut travailler d'abord ! *(To NAIN 5)* Qu'est-ce que tu vas faire ?
NAIN 5:	Je vais jardiner. *(Pretends to dig the garden)*
BLANCHE-NEIGE:	Et toi ?
NAIN 6:	Je vais balayer. *(Sweeps)*
BLANCHE-NEIGE:	Et toi ?
NAIN 7:	Je vais nettoyer. *(Cleans and dusts)*
BLANCHE-NEIGE:	Et toi ?
NAIN 1:	Je vais faire les lits. *(Makes the beds)*
BLANCHE-NEIGE:	Et toi ?
NAIN 2:	Je vais mettre la table. *(Lays the table)*
BLANCHE-NEIGE:	Et toi ?
NAIN 3:	Je vais bricoler. *(Pretends to fix shelves)*
BLANCHE-NEIGE:	Et toi ?
NAIN 4:	Je vais tricoter. *(Gets out knitting. They all work for a few seconds)*
BLANCHE-NEIGE:	À table. *(Calls them to eat, they come and sit down)*

TOUS LES NAINS:	Mmm, ça sent bon. Délicieux !

They all eat, then BLANCHE-NEIGE asks each of them about their hobbies

BLANCHE-NEIGE:	Qu'est-ce que tu aimes faire ?
NAIN 1:	J'aime lire.
BLANCHE-NEIGE:	Et toi ?
NAIN 2:	J'aime les cartes.
BLANCHE-NEIGE:	Et toi ?
NAIN 3:	J'aime la musique.
BLANCHE-NEIGE:	Et toi ?
NAIN 4:	J'aime le cinéma.
BLANCHE-NEIGE:	Et toi ?
NAIN 5:	J'aime le théâtre.
NAIN 6:	Et toi, Blanche-Neige, qu'est-ce que tu aimes faire ?
BLANCHE-NEIGE:	Moi, j'aime jouer du piano, faire la cuisine et jouer au golf !
TOUS LES NAINS:	*(Look pleased)* Au golf, super !
BLANCHE-NEIGE:	Et toi ?
NAIN 7:	Moi, j'aime dormir ! *(Pretends to sleep)*
TOUS LES NAINS:	Et moi. *(They pretend to sleep too)*

BLANCHE-NEIGE blows them all a kiss goodnight. Then VIEILLE DAME (old lady) knocks at the door with an apple. BLANCHE-NEIGE opens the door and looks surprised

VIEILLE DAME:	Une pomme mademoiselle ?
BLANCHE-NEIGE:	Oui, j'adore les pommes. *(Takes a bite and falls asleep, VIEILLE DAME goes off cackling)*

TOUS LES NAINS wake up slowly and look upset when they see BLANCHE-NEIGE lying down, apparently unconscious

NAIN 1:	Blanche-Neige !
NAIN 2:	Elle est fatiguée.
TOUS LES NAINS:	Oui. *(All nod, looking concerned)*
NAIN 3:	Elle a trop travaillé !
TOUS LES NAINS:	Oui. *(All nod again)*

NAIN 4:	Elle a fait trop de sport !
TOUS LES NAINS:	Oui. *(All nod again)*
NAIN 7:	Elle a trop regardé la télé.
TOUS LES NAINS:	Oui ... . *(They all nod in agreement then, look crossly at NAIN 7)* Non !
NAIN 6:	Regardez – la pomme. *(Smells it and makes a face, they all gasp and start running around in a panic bumping into each other, then sit in a curve around BLANCHE-NEIGE, on knees praying)*

PRINCE arrives riding his horse. He is lost and knocks on door. NAIN 6 answers door

PRINCE:	Je suis perdu. Où est le centre sportif s'il vous plaît ?
NAIN 6:	C'est là bas. *(Points to the distance but won't let the PRINCE leave)* Mais, attendez, vous êtes un prince ?
PRINCE:	*(Proudly)* Oui, je suis un prince.
NAIN 5:	*(Tries desperately to get PRINCE to kiss BLANCHE-NEIGE)* Alors ... embrassez la fille.
PRINCE:	Embrassez la fille ? Impossible ! Mais ... elle est belle ... elle est charmante ... . *(He starts to change his mind, pacing back and forth, glancing at BLANCHE-NEIGE, TOUS LES NAINS nod at what he says)* Elle est sportive ?
TOUS LES NAINS:	Oui, oui très sportive !
NAIN 4:	Elle joue au volley. *(PRINCE nods approvingly at each sport)*
NAIN 3:	Elle joue au basket.
NAIN 2:	Elle joue au golf !
NAIN 7:	Elle joue du piano. *(PRINCE looks confused at this)*
PRINCE:	D'accord. Je l'embrasse ! *(Kisses her, she wakes up and they look happy)*
TOUS LES NAINS:	C'est l'amour ? Oui, oui, c'est l'amour !

Everyone takes a bow

FIN

Wendy
part en vacances

La tour de Pise

Wendy part en vacances

A new adventure for Wendy and her friends. The play opens with Wendy excitedly preparing for her holiday which doesn't turn out quite as she planned. However, she enjoys meeting several well-known characters at the airport, one of whom can fly, which can be very useful if bad weather cancels your flight! Keep a lookout too for the pirate captain and crocodile who behave in a rather unexpected fashion!

Theme	
Holidays	
Language focus	
Key phrases about holidays in the present tense, future tense and past tense. Vocabulary for holiday activities, weather, and transport.	
Personnages	
Wendy	Wendy
Maman	Mum
Michel	Michael
Garçon Perdu	Lost Boy
Sirène	Mermaid
Fée	Fairy
Indien	Indian
Capitaine des pirates	Pirate captain
Crocodile	Crocodile
Pierre la Poêle	Peter Pan
Homme	This person can do several roles – conducteur (taxi driver), airport worker, sign carrier
Présentateur de télévision	Weather forecaster and news presenter
Costumes and props	
Holiday items: small suitcase, rucksack, map, ticket.	
Costumes for characters, including crocodile mask or hood.	
TV box frame.	
Alarm clocks x 2, one real, another made of foam for crocodile to 'swallow'.	
Phones, Disney souvenirs and postcard.	
Plastic cocktail "glasses" with umbrellas.	
Sign of an aeroplane crossed out. Sign for "Une semaine plus tard".	

Staging

Most of the action takes place in Wendy's house or at the airport. There needs to be a TV frame to one side all the way through for the presenter to sit behind. There should be a row of seats for the characters to sit on in all locations and enough room in front of them for the characters to 'fly' across the countryside. An adult needs to be on hand to operate the alarm clock. The waiter needs to come up behind the two characters in Scene 4 and hand the drinks over their shoulders.

Scene 1

At Wendy's home in London

WENDY:	*(Talks to audience excitedly jumps up and down, holds up air ticket)* Aujourd'hui je pars en vacances. Je suis impatiente ! ... Maman, où est ma valise ?
MAMAN:	La voilà !
WENDY:	Alors, t-shirt, lunettes, chapeau, réveil ... réveil ? *(Looks puzzled at MAMAN)*
MAMAN:	Oui, le réveil va sonner trente minutes avant le vol. Ne sois pas en retard ! *(MAMAN speaks strictly to WENDY and WENDY looks a bit worried)*

CONDUCTEUR (Taxi driver) knocks at the door, MAMAN answers

CONDUCTEUR:	Taxi pour l'aéroport ?
MAMAN:	Oui, merci ... Wendy, ton taxi est arrivé ! Dépêche-toi, le vol est à cinq heures.

WENDY jumps in taxi and goes off to airport

Scene 2

Waiting room of airport
Person sitting to the side at desk in box with frame of TV around them, getting increasingly sleepy until he/she drops off. WENDY gives ticket in at check-in desk. MICHEL is sitting. WENDY fidgets, then decides to start a conversation, first moving into the seat next to MICHEL

WENDY:	Je m'appelle Wendy, et toi ?
MICHEL:	Je m'appelle Michel. Où vas-tu ?
WENDY:	Je vais en Espagne, je vais bronzer. Et toi ?
MICHEL:	Je vais en Italie. Je vais visiter des monuments historiques.
WENDY:	C'est intéressant.

GARÇON PERDU (Lost Boy) arrives with rucksack and map, looking lost

WENDY:	Bonjour, où vas-tu ?

GARÇON PERDU:	Je vais faire du camping et je cherche la gare ... mais je suis perdu.
WENDY:	Ici, c'est l'aéroport !
GARÇON PERDU:	Oui, je sais ... je suis un garçon perdu ! *(He starts to cry loudly. WENDY comforts him)*

SIRÈNE (Mermaid) arrives and GARÇON PERDU stops crying. He and MICHEL look admiringly at her

MICHEL:	Elle est belle ! *(To GARÇON PERDU who nods in agreement)*
WENDY:	Où vas-tu ?
SIRÈNE:	Je vais à Hawaï. Je vais nager avec les dauphins.
GARÇON PERDU et MICHEL:	Génial !

INDIEN (Indian) arrives whooping, others look surprised but smile

INDIEN:	Bonjour r r r r ! *(Stretches into a whoop!)*
	Je vais au Canada, pour faire du kayak ! *(Mimes kayaking)*
TOUS:	Excellent ! *(All characters clap)*

FÉE (Fairy) arrives flying on energetically and happily

WENDY:	Bonjour, où vas-tu ?
FÉE:	Je vais à New York pour visiter les musées ... *(others look impressed, then FÉE adds as an aside to audience)* et faire du shopping. *(Others wave fingers disapprovingly at 'shopping')*

CAPITAINE DES PIRATES (Pirate Captain) arrives dramatically with his CROCODILE (crocodile) and addresses the audience

CAPITAINE DES PIRATES:	Je suis le Capitaine des Pirates ... *(others look afraid)* et voici mon crocodile !

Others who are now friends, run and hide behind chairs, then INDIEN comes cautiously out, taps CAPITAINE's shoulder and then jumps back

INDIEN:	Excusez-moi, vous allez où ?
CAPITAINE DES PIRATES:	Nous allons ... . *(Looks thoughtful)*
TOUS:	*(They look interested and start to come out)* Oui ... .

CAPITAINE DES PIRATES:	*(Louder)* Nous allons … .
TOUS:	*(More interested and louder)* Oui ?
CAPITAINE DES PIRATES:	*(Very loud)* Nous allons … .
TOUS:	*(Very loud)* Oui !
CAPITAINE DES PIRATES:	*(More quietly)* À Blackpool !
TOUS:	Blackpool ! *(They look at him crossly)*
CAPITAINE DES PIRATES:	Oui, nous allons danser et nager. *(Grabs CROCODILE and mimes dancing and swimming with him)*
GARÇON PERDU:	Vous allez danser avec un crocodile ?!
TOUS:	Oh là là. *(Make typical French gesture with hands)*

Alarm goes off

WENDY:	Zut ! Quatre heures et demie. Le vol ! *(Tries to switch off alarm but it won't switch off)*
CAPITAINE DES PIRATES:	Je peux vous aider ?

CAPITAINE DES PIRATES can't stop it either, so tosses it to CROCODILE who swallows it!

CROCODILE:	Mmm, c'est bon !
WENDY:	Mais … mon réveil ! *(Looks cross, pauses, sits, then looks bored)* Qu'est-ce qu'on fait ? On met la télé ?

WENDY switches TV on, person in box comes to life in the middle of forecast

PRÉSENTATEUR DE TÉLÉVISION:	… et voici la météo pour les vacances. *(Friends look interested and pleased, rub hands together)* Il pleut. *(Friends look a bit disappointed and mime rain)* Il fait froid. *(Friends mime cold and look grumpy, thumbs down)* Et il y a des tornades !
TOUS:	Des tornades ! *(All look at each other frightened, jump up and down, run round in circles)*

Airport worker runs on with announcement

HOMME:	Mesdames et messieurs, à cause du mauvais temps, il n'y a plus de vols aujourd'hui !
TOUS:	Plus de vols !

All stand up, look crossly at him and stick tongues out! He wags finger at them. PIERRE LA POÊLE (Peter Pan) arrives with flourish; all look surprised

PIERRE LA POÊLE:	Je suis Pierre la Poêle ! *(Stands proudly in a typical pose)*
FÉE et SIRÈNE:	Pierre La Poêle ! *(Pretend to feel faint)*
GARÇON PERDU et MICHEL:	C'est ridicule ! *(They tut at girls)*
PIERRE LA POÊLE:	Ne vous inquiétez pas, je sais voler !

PIERRE LA POÊLE flies across stage, while the others sing

TOUS:	Tu t'envoles, tu t'envoles, tu t'envoles, Pierre tu t'envoles.

PIERRE LA POÊLE grabs WENDY and she grabs MICHEL, they fly off, with FÉE and SIRÈNE too, around the stage

CAPITAINE DES PIRATES:	Taxi !

CAPITAINE, CROCODILE, INDIEN and GARÇON PERDU rush off stage to catch taxi

Scene 3

Flying over holiday locations

PIERRE LA POÊLE, WENDY, MICHEL, FÉE and SIRÈNE fly over rooftops and countryside and look down at characters doing holiday activities

WENDY:	Regardez, c'est Londres. Il y a beaucoup de touristes. Ils prennent des photos.
MICHEL:	Et voici le camping. On joue au volley. On fait un barbecue. *(All wave to campers)*
PIERRE LA POÊLE:	C'est la plage. On fait des baignades et du ski nautique. C'est super ! *(All wave)*

WENDY:	On traverse la Manche. Regardez les bateaux. Et voici la France ! *(All wave)*
SIRÈNE:	C'est Paris. On visite la tour Eiffel et Notre-Dame. *(All wave)*
PIERRE LA POÊLE:	Voilà, on est arrivé ... c'est Disneyland !
TOUS:	Disneyland ! C'est cool !
WENDY:	Toute ma vie, j'ai rêvé de passer des vacances à Disneyland !

She jumps up and down excitedly; they all go off singing (to the tune of Twinkle twinkle little star)

TOUS:	La magie est partout ... laissez commencer la magie. *(x2)*

Someone shows sign saying 'Une semaine plus tard'

Scene 4

At Wendy's home in London

WENDY arrives home with PIERRE LA POÊLE, FÉE, MICHEL and SIRÈNE and souvenirs such as Disney Mickey ears. TV presenter falling asleep again

WENDY:	Toc, toc, toc.
MAMAN:	Wendy ! *(Kisses both cheeks and hands WENDY postcard)*
WENDY:	Merci. *(Glances at card and sits)*

MAMAN kisses all others except PIERRE LA POÊLE who refuses!

MAMAN:	Alors, les vacances, c'était bien ? *(All sit)*
WENDY:	Oui, nous sommes allés à Disneyland. Nous avons joué, dansé, chanté.
SIRÈNE:	Nous sommes allés sur le train fantôme.

Others pretend to be ghosts, SIRÈNE looks scared

MICHEL:	Nous avons regardé des spectacles.
FÉE:	Nous avons acheté des souvenirs.
PIERRE LA POÊLE:	Nous avons mangé des glaces ... miam, miam.

Phone rings, MICHEL answers, GARÇON PERDU at side of stage as if somewhere else

---

MICHEL:	Allô.
GARÇON PERDU:	Allô ... Michel ? Comment ça va ?
MICHEL:	Ça va très bien, merci. Où êtes vous ?
GARÇON PERDU:	Nous sommes en Espagne. Nous faisons du camping. Nous avons pris le train. C'était rapide.
MICHEL:	Ah, oui.
GARÇON PERDU:	Nous avons bronzé, nagé, pêché.
MICHEL:	Bonne fin de vacances. Au revoir !
GARÇON PERDU:	Au revoir.

WENDY's phone rings and she answers

WENDY:	Allô.
INDIEN:	Allô ... c'est Wendy ? Ça va ?
WENDY:	Oui merci ... alors, les vacances ?
INDIEN:	Je suis allé en Suisse en train. J'ai fait des promenades et du canoë.
WENDY:	Super ... . Merci pour la carte postale. Au revoir !

All characters relax on sofa and decide to watch TV

SIRÈNE:	On met la télé ?
TOUS:	Oui *(all enthusiastic; SIRÈNE switches on TV)*
PRÉSENTATEUR DE TÉLÉVISION:	Et voici les actualités : Oh, là là, là là là. Crocodile trouvé à la plage de Blackpool ! Tous les touristes sont parties !

All look scared and run off at mention of tourists leaving. CAPITAINE and CROCODILE come on as if on beach. They relax back to back and waiter hands cocktails over their shoulders

CAPITAINE DES PIRATES:	C'est bien les vacances.
TOUS:	Oui, c'est bien les vacances !

Everyone comes back on stage to take a bow

FIN

Les trois petits cochons vont à l'école

Les trois petits cochons vont à l'école

Mummy and Daddy Pig love their children but are looking forward to some peace and quiet when they leave home. So, the three little pigs are sent off to school to learn to build houses. But, of course, things don't always go to plan and the pigs just don't get what school is all about ... . And then there are the teachers to contend with who are hiding their true identity as, you guessed it, wolves!

Theme	
School	
Language focus	
Phrases about school subjects, likes and dislikes, strengths and weaknesses. Comments about subjects and teachers' personalities. Adjectives. School-bag items. Routine of school day. Time.	
Personnages	
Cochon 1	Pig 1 (oldest brother, good leader. More sensible, likes academic subjects)
Cochon 2	Pig 2 (enthusiastic)
Cochon 3	Pig 3 (not very bright, likes food, gives silly answers – comic role)
Maman	Mum (happy to have peace and quiet when the pigs leave home)
Papa	Dad (also looking forward to children leaving!)
Prof de maths	Maths teacher (gets impatient easily with silly pupils)
Prof de musique	Music teacher (also gets impatient)
Prof de sport	PE teacher (can't wait for the end of the lesson)
Prof d'histoire	History teacher (points out that pigs often get eaten and end up as sausages)
Prof de bricolage	DIY teacher (kind to pupils, teaches them how to make things)
Costumes and props	

Piggy and wolf hoods, teachers' graduation robes (if available), or other smart clothes.
Wine bottle and glasses (plastic).
Rucksacks and pencil-case items.
Large cards with subject words (*Les maths*; *La musique*; *Le sport*; *L'histoire*; *Le bricolage*) on them and sign for '*l'École Mange Tout*'.
Plastic biscuits or pictures of them.
Picture of pork roasting on a spit in a thought bubble.
Portrait of Henry VIII.
Picture of Henry VIII's six wives (in wedding dresses if possible).
Clock and bell.
Ball.
Model houses made of straw, twigs and bricks.
Sign saying '*Trois heures plus tard*'.

Staging

This play simply needs a few chairs for the home scenes and a couple of rows of chairs for the school scenes. Leave room at the front for the pigs to play ball and run across the stage a few times.

Scene 1

At home

PAPA ET MAMAN: Les enfants, venez ici ! *(COCHONS (Pigs) scurry in and stand to attention)*

PAPA: Nous avons decidé ... *(MAMAN and PAPA pace up and down as they say each bit)*

MAMAN: ... qu'il est temps ...

PAPA: ... que vous partiez de chez nous ! *(COCHONS look scared and snort)*

MAMAN: Vous allez construire vos propres maisons !

COCHONS: Hourrah ! *(Excited ... then worried)*

COCHONS 1: Mais comment ?

PAPA: Vous allez apprendre ça à l'école !

COCHONS: Hourrah ... à l'école ? *(Enthusiastic at first, then unsure)*

MAMAN: Oui, vous allez apprendre les maths ... . *(COCHONS all count on fingers, looking puzzled)*

PAPA: La musique ... . *(COCHONS mime playing violins, recorders, guitars etc)*

MAMAN: Le sport ... . *(Mime running and other sports)*

PAPA: Et l'histoire.

COCHONS: Excellent ! *(All clap and nod in agreement)*

PAPA: Travaillez bien, mais ... attention aux loups !

COCHONS: Loups ! *(They gasp and look scared)*

MAMAN: Oui, il y'en a partout !

PAPA: Au revoir les enfants !

COCHONS leave home with rucksacks

COCHONS: *(Sing to tune of 'Il est né le divin Enfant')*
Qui a peur du grand méchant loup ?
En tout cas c'est sûrement pas nous. *(x2)*

MAMAN and PAPA get out a bottle of wine and start relaxing

PAPA: Du vin rouge chérie ?

MAMAN: Merci chéri.

Scene 2

At school. COCHONS arrive at l'École Mange Tout

COCHON 3:	L'École Mange Tout, super !
COCHON 1:	Vérifiez vos sacs. *(They stand to attention and hold up each item)*
	Règle ... crayon ... gomme. On y va!

Leçon 1: Les maths

COCHON 2 sees timetable posted and takes it down to read; the others look over his/her shoulder

COCHON 2:	Voici l'emploi du temps. Première leçon, c'est les maths !
COCHON 3:	Les maths ? Ah non ! C'est difficile ! Je suis très faible en maths.
PROF DE MATHS:	Bonjour, les cochons, asseyez-vous ! *(Holds up pictures of biscuits or plastic ones)* Alors, 3 biscuits et 2 biscuits. Ça fait combien en tout ?

COCHONS think and count on fingers, then COCHON 3 puts hand up, excitedly

PROF DE MATHS:	Oui ?
COCHON 3:	Zéro ! On a tout mangé ! *(Others laugh)*
PROF DE MATHS:	Imbéciles ! Vous êtes nuls en maths ! *(COCHONS look ashamed and run off)*
COCHON 1:	Oh là là ... le prof est strict !

Leçon 2: La musique

COCHON 1:	C'est quelle leçon maintenant ?
COCHON 2:	Musique. J'adore la musique. C'est ma matière préférée. J'espère que la prof est gentille !
PROF DE MUSIQUE:	Bonjour la classe ! Aujourd'hui, on va chanter !
COCHON 2:	Hourrah ! J'adore chanter !
COCHONS:	La la la. *(COCHONS sing really badly)*
PROF DE MUSIQUE:	Non, non, non ! Écoutez et répétez :
	Do ré mi fa sol la si do. *(Points to them in turn)*
COCHON 1:	*(Sings well)* Do ré mi fa sol la si do.

COCHON 2:	*(Sings well)* Do ré mi fa sol la si do.
COCHON 3:	*(Sings badly)* Sol mi ré do si fa do. *(Other COCHONS stare at him)* Je suis faible en musique.

Others look sympathetic and try to cheer COCHON 3 up; he looks happier

COCHON 1:	Ce n'est pas vrai.
PROF DE MUSIQUE:	Si, c'est vrai, tu es nul en musique.
COCHON 1 et 2:	Vous n'êtes pas sympa ! *(They look crossly at PROF!)*
COCHON 3:	La prof est sévère !

Leçon 3: Le sport

COCHON 1:	C'est quelle leçon maintenant ? *(They look at timetable)*
COCHON 3:	Le sport ! J'espère que le prof est rigolo.
PROF DE SPORT:	Aujourd'hui on va jouer au volley. *(Throws ball to COCHON 2)*
COCHON 2:	Chouette ! J'adore jouer au volley. *(Bounces ball, others join in)*
COCHON 1:	C'est bon ? *(To PROF, who shakes his head and looks cross)*
COCHON 3:	J'aime le sport. C'est ma matière préférée. *(COCHONS mess about and pass ball to each other under their chins, through their legs, etc)*
PROF DE SPORT:	Oh là là ... le cours finit à quelle heure ? *(Looks at watch in despair)*

Bell rings for break

PROF DE SPORT:	Merci ! *(To the bell)*
COCHONS:	C'est la récré !

PROFS all collapse in chairs in staff room, COCHONS go to play

PROF DE MATHS:	Oh là là ... les cochons.
PROF DE MUSIQUE:	C'est incroyable ... ils sont idiots !
PROF DE SPORT:	Oui, mais pensez au porc rôti.

PROF D'HISTOIRE holds up picture of a roast pork joint inside a thought bubble

TOUS LES PROFS:	Mmm, c'est délicieux !

Bell for end of break, COCHONS come back on stage

COCHON 3:	C'est quelle leçon maintenant ?
COCHON 2:	Histoire !
COCHON 1:	Génial ! J'adore l'histoire ! C'est très intéressant. J'espère que le prof est sympa.

Leçon 4: L'histoire

PROF D'HISTOIRE:	Aujourd'hui, nous allons étudier les rois anglais. Henry Huit. Il était comment ? *(Holds up portrait of Henry VIII)*
COCHON 2:	Il avait six femmes. *(Looks at picture of Henry VIII's six wives; others look amazed)*
COCHONS 1 et 3:	Six !
PROF D'HISTOIRE:	Oui. *(Looks interested and pleased)*
COCHON 1:	Il était gros.
PROF D'HISTOIRE:	Oui. *(Looks less pleased)*
COCHON 3:	Et il aimait beaucoup manger … *(hesitates as he/she tries to think)* le poulet, le poisson et le boeuf … .
PROF D'HISTOIRE:	*(Looks annoyed now)* Oui … et les saucisses ! *(COCHON 3 nods, COCHONS 1 and 2 amazed at COCHON 3 who doesn't get it)*
COCHONS 1 et 2:	Les saucisses ! *(COCHON 3 looks confused)* Les cochons ! *(COCHON 3 understands now and looks scared)*
COCHON 3:	Aïe !

All PROFS appear as wolves now

COCHONS:	Les loups ! Au secours !

COCHONS run off screaming, chased by wolves, then slow down to slow motion movement. COCHON 1 stops the others

COCHON 1:	Qui a peur des loups ?

COCHONS pause

COCHONS 2 et 3:	Pas nous !

All COCHONS turn around, paw at ground, then stick tongues out, scaring wolves off. COCHONS collapse in heap on floor and look tired and relieved, then suddenly remember they haven't made their houses

COCHONS: Les maisons !

A few moments later they see PROF DE BRICOLAGE (DIY teacher) pass by

COCHON 3:   Excusez-nous ! Vous êtes un professeur ?

PROF DE BRICOLAGE:

       Oui.

COCHON 2:   De quelle matière ?

PROF DE BRICOLAGE:

       Bricolage.

COCHONS: Bricolage ! Excellent !

COCHON 1:   Pouvez-vous nous aider à construire des maisons ?

PROF DE BRICOLAGE:

       Oui, bien sûr !

They go off together to make their houses. Then another pupil goes across stage with clock/sign saying 'Trois heures plus tard'. COCHONS bring their model houses on.

PROF DE BRICOLAGE:

       Voilà ! Vous êtes très forts en bricolage.

COCHONS: Merci beaucoup, Monsieur Bricoleur.

Scene 3

At home
COCHONS go off and reappear with model houses hidden behind their backs and head for home where they find MAMAN and PAPA relaxing and looking surprised to see them. They jump up, hastily hiding wine!

MAMAN: Vous êtes de retour ? *(Not very pleased!)*

COCHONS: Oui.

PAPA: Qu'est-ce que vous avez appris ?

COCHONS: Les maths, la musique, le sport, l'histoire et le bricolage !

MAMAN: Le bricolage ? *(Looks pleased)*

COCHONS:	Oui, voici les maisons ! *(They show model houses)*
MAMAN:	*(Starts enthusiastically but voice tails off. She's not really very happy to see them!)* Elles sont ... très ... belles.

COCHONS go off looking happy

MAMAN et PAPA:	Oh là là. Ils ne vont jamais partir !

COCHONS come back singing to tune of 'Il est né le divin Enfant'

COCHONS:	Qui a peur du grand méchant loup ? En tout cas c'est sûrement pas nous. (x 2)

Everyone takes a bow

FIN

Dorothée fait les courses

Centre commercial
Émeraude

Dorothée fait les courses

Dorothée meets familiar characters from Oz and takes them shopping for the things they need. The tornado delivers tickets to the Emerald Shopping Centre where Dorothée hopes to find a bargain in the sales!

Theme	
Shopping	
Language focus	
Food, clothes, key shopping phrases. Some phrases in the past tense. A fair amount of more advanced sentence structure.	
Personnages	
Tante Emma	Aunt Emma
Oncle	Uncle
Fermiers x 2	2 farmhands (not very clever!)
Dorothée	Dorothy
Lion	Lion
Magicien	Magician
Épouvantail	Scarecrow
Souris	Mouse
L'Homme d'Étain	Tin Man
Fille d'Étain	Tin Girl
Marchands x 6	Stallholders (could double up)
Sorcière	Witch
Costumes and props	
Suitable costumes for characters, masks or hoods for lion and mouse, green wigs for stallholders, red shoes. Basket with plastic food. Green tickets. Wand and purses x 2 Wilting flowers, plastic brains, hearts, box of "courage", plastic bread and fruit. Newspaper. Table, chairs, market stalls.	
Staging	
An outside scene for most of the action with a market stall on one side. The actors need to be the tornado by whirling around Dorothée, but wind sound effects would definitely enhance this.	

Scene 1

At the farm

TANTE EMMA (Aunt Emma), ONCLE (Uncle), FERMIERS 1 and 2 (Farmhands 1 and 2) already on stage as DOROTHÉE (Dorothy) arrives

TANTE EMMA:	Dorothée, Dorothée, où es-tu ?
DOROTHÉE:	Salut, je suis là !
TANTE EMMA:	Où as-tu été ?
DOROTHÉE:	Je suis allée au magasin (comme tu me l'as demandé).
TANTE EMMA:	Qu'est-ce que tu as acheté ?
DOROTHÉE:	J'ai acheté du fromage, du beurre, du jambon ... .
TANTE EMMA:	*(Increasingly cross)* Et les tomates ? Les pommes ? Les champignons ?
DOROTHÉE:	Oh là là, je les ai oubliés. Je suis désolée. *(Pauses)* Ne t'inquiète-pas, je vais les chercher au marché.

DOROTHÉE starts to move away from centre stage as if she is going to go back to the shops. ONCLE and the two silly FERMIERS look at the sky and discuss impending tornado, finally looking scared

ONCLE:	Non, Dorothée, il y a du vent, c'est dangereux.
FERMIER 1:	Regardez le ciel.
FERMIER 2:	Ce n'est pas bon.
FERMIER 1:	Ce n'est pas bon du tout.
FERMIER 2:	Il y aura une tornade ?
FERMIER 1:	Je pense que oui ... j'ai peur.
FERMIER 2:	Au secours !

FERMIERS run around and look scared, ONCLE looks irritated

ONCLE:	Oh là là !
DOROTHÉE:	Au revoir, je reviens dans cinq minutes !
ONCLE:	Non, attends ! *(ONCLE tries to stop DOROTHÉE but isn't quick enough)*

Scene 2

En route

All exit stage except DOROTHÉE who wanders back and forth as if she is going back to the shops, then the tornado arrives – most of the cast whirl around her pretending to be tornado, she finally collapses and falls asleep, they drop green tickets all around her. She wakes up and picks up a ticket

DOROTHÉE: *(Yawns)* Qu'est-ce que c'est ? *(Pauses and holds up ticket)* Centre commercial Émeraude ... soldes ... réduction de cinquante pour cent ! *(Very enthusiastic – she loves sales!)* Génial ! J'adore les soldes.

Skips off singing to the tune of French national anthem

DOROTHÉE: Alors allons au centre commercial
Le jour du shopping est arrivé

ÉPOUVANTAIL (Scarecrow) comes on from other side and stands still in typical pose. SORCIÈRE (Witch) also comes on, rubs hands together excitedly

SORCIÈRE: Soldes ? Réductions ? J'y vais aussi. *(Then goes off cackling)* Hé, hé, hé ... .

After a pause DOROTHÉE comes on and notices ÉPOUVANTAIL

DOROTHÉE: Excusez-moi, où est le centre commercial Émeraude s'il vous plait ?

ÉPOUVANTAIL: C'est par là. *(Swings hands left, then right. DOROTHÉE notices)*

DOROTHÉE: C'est par là ou c'est par là ? *(Becoming slightly cross, points left then right)*

ÉPOUVANTAIL: C'est par là. *(Swings arms across each other to point in both directions)*

DOROTHÉE: *(Really cross)* C'est ridicule, vous êtes idiot !

ÉPOUVANTAIL: Oui je suis très idiot ... . Je n'ai pas de cerveau.

DOROTHÉE: Tu n'as pas de cerveau ?! *(Surprised, but not cross now, pauses, walks away then comes back)* Tu aimes faire du shopping ?

ÉPOUVANTAIL: Oui ... . Non ... . Bof ... je ne sais pas ! *(Scratches head and answers hesitantly)*

DOROTHÉE: *(Firmly)* Viens au centre commercial. On va acheter un cerveau.

They go off singing 'Alors allons au centre commercial' as before and come back on. Next they find LION (Lion) crying by a tree frightened by SOURIS (Mouse)

DOROTHÉE:	Qu'est-ce qu'il y a ? Vous avez peur d'une souris ?
LION:	Oui je n'ai pas de courage.
SOURIS:	*(Threatens LION)* L'argent ou la vie ?!
LION:	L'argent, l'argent, ne me tue pas !

LION tries to give purse to SOURIS, but DOROTHÉE stops him and takes him by the hand

DOROTHÉE:	Non ! Viens au centre commercial, on va acheter du courage.
ÉPOUVANTAIL:	*(To SOURIS)* Bouh !

They all go off singing as before. They come across HOMME D'ÉTAIN (Tin Man)

HOMME D'ÉTAIN:	Excusez-moi, vous allez au centre commercial ?
DOROTHÉE:	Oui. Qu'est-ce que vous cherchez ?
HOMME D'ÉTAIN:	Je voudrais acheter un cœur ... parce que ... je n'en ai pas !
DOROTHÉE:	Le pauvre ! Viens !

SORCIÈRE creeps back across the stage unnoticed

SORCIÈRE:	*(Scornfully)* Et moi, je vais acheter des coeurs et des cerveaux pour faire de la soupe !

Scene 3

In the Emerald Shopping Centre
They sing again and arrive at the Emerald Shopping Centre. They look excited when they see the sign

TOUS:	Centre commercial, on est arrivé ! Tous aux portefeuilles !

MARCHANDS (Stallholders) trying to sell their fruit/bread/flowers to the four friends

MARCHAND 1:	*(Loudly)* Des pêches, des poires, des oranges.
ÉPOUVANTAIL:	Ah non, elles ne sont pas bonnes.
MARCHAND 2:	Du bon pain frais ... des croissants ... des gâteaux.
LION:	C'est trop cher !
MARCHAND 3:	Achetez des fleurs ici : roses, violettes, tulipes. *(Points to old dying flowers)*

HOMME D'ÉTAIN:	*(Looks shocked)* Elles sont mortes !
DOROTHÉE, LION et ÉPOUVANTAIL:	*(They all gasp loudly and make cross sign)* Mortes !

Pause

LION:	Où est-ce qu'on va acheter du courage, un cerveau et un cœur ?
HOMME D'ÉTAIN:	Je ne sais pas … . Il n'y a rien ici.
ÉPOUVANTAIL:	Et toi, Dorothée, qu'est-ce que tu veux acheter ?
DOROTHÉE:	Des chaussures … . Des chaussures rouges !

SORCIÈRE overhears this and creeps across back of stage again

SORCIÈRE:	Des chaussures ? J'adore les chaussures … mais, je n'ai pas d'argent. *(Pulls out empty pockets)*
MARCHAND 4:	Courage, courage, venez acheter du courage ici.

All four friends jump up in excitement

DOROTHÉE:	Courage ! Lion, va acheter du courage. *(Urges him on)*
LION:	Ah non, j'ai peur.
ÉPOUVANTAIL:	Lion, vas-y. Achète du courage ! *(Speaks firmly, pushes LION forward)*
LION:	Non, je ne peux pas. C'est trop cher … c'est dangereux !

MAGICIEN (Magician) arrives dramatically

MAGICIEN:	Je peux vous aider ?
LION:	J'ai besoin de courage mais je ne veux pas l'acheter. Le marchand est très féroce !
MAGICIEN:	*(Waves wand around pretending to do magic)* Allez hop !
LION:	*(Lion not so scared now magic has worked)* C'est combien pour le courage ?
MARCHAND 4:	Un euro.
LION:	Un euro ! Ce n'est pas cher du tout. *(Pays his money, MARCHAND 4 gives him courage in a box which he swallows. He instantly flexes his muscles and goes up to all the MARCHANDS)* Bouh ! Bouh ! Bouh !

MARCHAND 5:	Des cerveaux, des cerveaux, des petits, des grands !
DOROTHÉE:	Va acheter un cerveau ! *(DOROTHÉE urges ÉPOUVANTAIL to buy a brain)*

ÉPOUVANTAIL looks at all the brains, picking them up and commenting on them

ÉPOUVANTAIL:	C'est trop grand ... . C'est trop petit ... . C'est parfait ! Ça me va ?

Pretends to try it on his head, it breaks through hole in his old hat

DOROTHÉE:	Oui, c'est génial !

ÉPOUVANTAIL hands over the money, gets his brain and does intelligent things, like reading newspaper

FILLE D'ÉTAIN:	Des cœurs, des cœurs.

DOROTHÉE hears and nudges HOMME D'ÉTAIN

DOROTHÉE:	Va acheter un cœur.
FILLE D'ÉTAIN:	Des cœurs roses, des cœurs violets, pas chers du tout.
	Réduits de cinquante pour cent.

SORCIÈRE creeps up behind and secretly steals purse from the pocket of HOMME D'ÉTAIN. MAGICIEN notices. HOMME D'ÉTAIN sees FILLE D'ÉTAIN (Tin Girl) and feels shy as he likes her

FILLE D'ÉTAIN:	Tu veux acheter un cœur ?
HOMME D'ÉTAIN:	Oui ... non ... . *(Turns to the others)* Elle est très belle !
DOROTHÉE:	Vas-y ! *(Encourages him)*
FILLE D'ÉTAIN:	Seulement quatre euros !
HOMME D'ÉTAIN:	*(Tries to find money)* J'ai perdu mon argent.
FILLE D'ÉTAIN:	Ce n'est pas grave. Tu es très beau. Je te le donne ! *(They look lovingly at each other!)*

MAGICIEN catches SORCIÈRE and gets her to hand over purse

MAGICIEN:	*(To SORCIÈRE)* Le porte-monnaie !
	Vous avez perdu quelque-chose ? *(Hands purse back to HOMME D'ÉTAIN)*

HOMME D'ÉTAIN: Oui, mon porte-monnaie … . Ah merci !

HOMME D'ÉTAIN and FILLE D'ÉTAIN look happy together. MAGICIEN takes SORCIÈRE off

**DOROTHÉE et
ÉPOUVANTAIL:**   C'est l'amour ! Aah !

MARCHAND 6:   Des chaussures, très jolies !

DOROTHÉE jumps up excitedly

DOROTHÉE: Vous avez des chaussures rouges ?

MARCHAND 6:   Oui, vous faites quelle pointure ?

DOROTHÉE: Trente-sept … . Merci … elles sont très jolies.

DOROTHÉE and others sit down pleased. She speaks to each friend in turn

DOROTHÉE: Alors toi, tu as ton cerveau, et toi ton courage et toi ton cœur, et moi, mes chaussures. Maintenant je veux retourner chez moi. *(Puts on shoes and finds they are magical)* Les chaussures sont magiques ! Chez moi, chez moi, chez moi !

DOROTHÉE spins off they all wave good bye

TOUS: Au revoir, Dorothée.

Everyone enters back on stage and takes a bow!

FIN

English versions

This collection of plays was written initially in French, focusing on incorporating useful phrases that pupils might already know or would benefit from learning.

These versions were completed after the French and are designed to read well in English. Hopefully they will also help the comprehension of any pupils that are struggling with a particular phrase. The traditional songs have been kept in French. They could be replaced by well-known English songs.

Cinderella (Cendrillon)

Scene 1

Cinderella's house
Cat is asleep by the fire. Spider is annoying the cat by tickling him
Enter Cinderella with broom sweeping up. She is wearing an old overall with a pretty dress underneath.
Spider sees Cinderella arrive with her broom and is afraid

Spider:	I'm afraid ... help!
Cinderella:	I work, I work ... I'm so tired!
	(She looks tired and wipes her hand over her forehead. Mice come on stage and do the same)
Mice:	I work, I work, I'm so tired!
Cat:	You mice are so naughty! *(Cat takes broom from Cinderella, tells mice off and chases them off stage with the broom)*

Mice run off, scared by the cat, then come back on, sit Cinderella down and bring her a cup of tea. Cat goes back to sleep by fire

Mouse 1:	Sit down Cinderella.
Mouse 2:	Have a cup of tea.
Cinderella:	Mmm, it's good.

Ugly Sisters arrive, hungry and cross, stamping feet. When Cinderella hears them coming, she runs off

Sister 1:	I'm hungry.
Sister 2:	I'm thirsty.
Sisters:	Cinderella!
Sister 1:	Bring me bread. *(Cinderella runs back and forth bringing items)*
Sister 2:	And Camembert!
Sister 1:	And red wine!

Mice are interested in idea of cheese and wine

Mouse 1:	Camembert! That's cheese! Yum, yum!
Mouse 2:	Red wine? I love it! *(Pretends to be drunk!)*
Cat:	It's not good for mice! Meow!
Spider:	No, but it's very good for spiders! *(Tries to get the bottle)*

Fairy Godmother arrives

Fairy Godmother:	Knock, knock, knock!
Sister 1:	Who's there?
Sister 2:	Open the door.
Fairy Godmother:	Hello girls!

Sister 1:	Oh no, not you ... .
	(In a nasty voice, imitating the Fairy Godmother) Do the washing up ... .
Sister 2:	*(In a nasty voice, imitating the Fairy Godmother)* Do the cooking ... .
Fairy Godmother:	*(Crossly)* You are both very lazy and very naughty!
Sisters:	Yes, that's true! *(They sit down and put their feet up, proud of being lazy)*

Postman arrives

Postman:	Knock, knock, knock.
Sisters:	Again? Cinderella, open the door. *(They jump up and then push Cinderella to the door)*
Cinderella:	Good morning, Sir.

Postman gives invitation to Cinderella

Postman:	An invitation for you all.
Cinderella:	Thank you.

One of the Sisters snatches it before Cinderella has a chance to read it. Cinderella moves back

Sister 1:	An invitation ... .
Sister 2:	To the ball ... .
Sister 1:	At the Palace of Versailles ... .
Sister 2:	Saturday? That's tomorrow!

Sisters run around panicking about their hair, clothes, shoes and nails. Cinderella runs over and tries to help them get ready

Sister 1:	My hair!
Sister 2:	My dress!
Sister 1:	My shoes!
Sister 2:	My nails!

Sisters go off still fussing and muttering. Cinderella sits sadly by the fire, Mice try to comfort her

Cinderella:	I love dancing, but ... I can't go to the ball ... .
Mouse 1:	Don't worry Cinderella.

Fairy Godmother arrives with a wand, others look surprised

Fairy Godmother:	Cinderella, you shall go to the ball.
Cinderella:	But look at my dress.
Fairy Godmother:	Pouf! *(Waves wand and Mice pull overalls from Cinderella to reveal pretty dress)*
Mouse 1:	It's very pretty.
Mouse 2:	You look beautiful!

Fairy Godmother waves her wand at Mice

Fairy Godmother: Pouf ... and pouf!

Mice, now changed into horses, 'gallop' around the stage and fetch the carriage
Mice: I'm a horse! I'm a horse!
Fairy Godmother: Have fun at the ball, Cinderella ... but when the clock strikes twelve, you must leave!

Cinderella gets in carriage. All three go back and forth across stage a few times

Scene 2

The Palace of Versailles
(Optional background music fading out as carriage stops)

Mouse 1:   Here is the Palace of Versailles!
Cinderella: It's amazing!

Cinderella steps out of the carriage and goes into the ballroom shyly. Meanwhile the Sisters are talking to the Prince
Sister 1:   I love your palace.
Sister 2:   How much do you earn?
Prince: More than you. *(They both turn away in a huff, leaving Cinderella in Prince's view. He is instantly smitten with Cinderella of course!)*
Prince: You are beautiful.
Cinderella: You are handsome.

They greet each other the French way (kissing on both cheeks)
Prince: Would you like to dance?
Cinderella: Yes, I would love to.

Play music and fade out (optional). They dance and all guests admire them. The Sisters dance together. Mice look on too, giggling excitedly
Mouse 1:   Is it love?
Mouse 2:   Yes it's love. *(They make kissing sounds)*

Clock strikes midnight
Cinderella: Midnight already!

Cinderella runs off, leaving shoe which Prince picks up, admires, then pauses and sniffs, pulls a face
Prince: Your shoe ... it's pretty ... *(sniffs)* it's smelly ... cheese!

Scene 3

Cinderella's house
Cinderella, changed back into rags, runs back on stage, sits by fire, sobbing. Mice by her feet. Sisters arrive
stomping on again

Sister 1:   Poor Cinderella.

Sister 2:   The ball was fabulous.

Sister 1:   The Prince was charming.

Prince: Knock, knock, knock.

Sisters: *(Sisters hear knock and look surprised)* It's the Prince! *(Gasp)*

Prince: *(Holding out the shoe to one of the Sisters)* Is this your shoe?

Sister 2:   It's too small. *(Looks cross and gives it back)*

Prince: *(To the other Sister)* Is this your shoe?

Sister 1:   It's too big!

Prince: *(To Cinderella)* Would you like to try?

Cinderella: Yes, I would.

Mice: It fits!

Prince: Will you marry me?

Mice throw veil over Cinderella's head

Cinderella: Yes! Good idea!

Prince and Cinderella look happy and pose as if for a wedding photograph

Fairy Godmother: Knock, knock, knock.

Sister 1:   *(Very crossly)* Who's there? *(Opens door and recognises Fairy Godmother)*

Sister 2:   *(Very crossly)* You again?! *(Both Sisters stick tongues out at her)*

Fairy Godmother: Now it's **your** turn to work! Pouf! *(Zaps them with wand and they are now hard-working. Other characters all stand in a line with arms crossed watching them work)*

Sisters: Let's get to work! *(They sweep and dust, then polish the other characters' shoes as they say left and right)*

Mouse 1:   Left. *(All put left foot forward to be cleaned)*

Mouse 2:   Right. *(All put right foot forward to be cleaned)*

Mouse 1 very quietly under breath counts to three so that all in the line-up can say in unison

All: Great! *(They make a triumphant gesture)*

The End

The Little Red Hen (La Petite Poule Rousse)

Scene 1

Farmyard scene
Hen sweeps the floor, other animals asleep, Cockerel announces morning

Cockerel:	Cock-a-doodle-doo! Cock-a-doodle-doo!
Hen:	*(To each animal)* Wake up.
Each animal in turn:	Sshh, I'm sleeping.

Hen sings 'Frère Jacques' to herself gradually getting louder and carries on sweeping, she shouts as she gets to 'Dormez-vous' and jumps at the end for 'Ding dang dong'

All the Animals:	Oh dear!

Animals wake up, hands over ears, then go grumpily to sit down at table

Pig:	I want my breakfast! *(Pounds fists on table)*
Sheep:	I want some cereal.
Cat:	Yes ... with milk. *(Looks hopefully at cow, who shakes her head)*
Cow:	I would like a croissant.
Duck:	Or a chocolate pastry ... mmm, I love those!
Hen:	Sorry, there isn't anything! *(Shows them empty cupboard, all animals look cross)*
Rat:	What are we going to do?
Hen:	We will have to work!
All the animals:	Work?!
Hen:	Yes. First, I'm going to sow some seeds. *(To all the animals)* Who will help me? Mr Cat, will you help me?
Cat:	Er ... *(pretends to think)* no.
Hen:	Mr Pig?
Pig:	Er ... no.
Hen:	Mr Rat?
Rat:	Er ... no.
Hen:	Mr Sheep?
Sheep:	Baa ... no.

She looks at each of the rest and they all shake their heads in turn and say 'no!' Hen mimes sowing the seeds, then goes to bed, as do all other animals. Cockerel crows for the next day

Cockerel:	Cock-a-doodle-doo!

Pupil brings on photograph of a field of corn grown tall. Hen wakes, looks pleased and rubs hands with glee

Hen:	Today, I am going to cut the corn. Who will help me? *(She looks hopefully at the animals, but they each have an excuse)*
Pig:	Not me. I'm having a wash. *(Washes face, others look surprised!)*
Duck:	Not me, I'm singing. *(Sings badly)* Meunier tu dors? Ton moulin, ton moulin, va trop vite … .
All the animals:	Sshh!
Hen:	And you?
Horse:	No, I'm dancing. *(Dances with cow who looks surprised)*
Cat:	No, I'm reading. *(Pretends to read, others impressed, nod)*
Rat:	No, I'm praying. *(Mimes praying, others look amazed, then cross themselves)*

Hen looks disappointed, but cuts the corn by herself and starts to look tired. She tries to pick up a large bag of corn but it's too heavy for her

Hen:	Who will help me?
Horse:	Not me, I'm sleeping. *(Snorts like a horse! Yawns and pretends to sleep with head on one side)*
Pig:	Not me, I'm running. *(Runs on spot)*
Cow:	Not me, I'm talking, blah, blah, blah. *(Chats to duck)*
Dog:	Not me, I'm playing with the sheep. *(Jumps about the Sheep and tries to get her to play but she isn't interested)*
Sheep:	Baa, baa.
Duck:	*(Pictures of sheep or toy sheep to be held up)* Not me, I'm counting sheep! 1, 2, 3, 4 … .

Duck counts sheep or lined up toy sheep, then Sheep runs to end of line of sheep to confuse Duck

Rat:	Not me, I'm looking for cheese! *(Sniffs about for cheese. Someone from the wings holds out a piece of cheese and he runs after it then comes back pleased)*
Cat:	Not me, I'm chasing rats! *(Paws at Rat with claws out, Rat runs off and hides with cheese)*

Hen grinds the corn, looking tired

Hen:	I'm going to make the dough. Who will help me?
All the animals:	Not me … not me … . *(All animals one after the other)*

Hen makes the dough and puts the bread in the oven to bake. Someone holds up sign saying '30 minutes later' or winds on the hands of a clock. Hen brings out a lovely fresh loaf

Hen:	It smells very good.
Pig:	Mmm, it smells so good. I'm hungry.

Each animal goes to Hen in turn and asks for bread

Dog:	Could I have some bread please?
Hen:	*(Thinks for a moment)* No, it's for my chicks.

Cow and all the others follow on with same request, ending with Rat

Rat:	Can I ... ? *(Before he can even start to speak, Hen interrupts)*
Hen:	No ! Come on chicks ... food's on the table.

Chicks come in and share the bread

Hen:	Would you like some bread?
Chicks:	Thanks Mum ... would you like some bread? *(Each Chick offers bread to the next one. Other animals look cross and hungry)*
Chicks:	Mmm, delicious! *(Rub tummies with satisfaction)*
Hen:	Are you going to work now? *(All animals nod their heads in shame)* Right then, sow the seeds. *(She gives them seeds, which they scatter)* Cut the corn. *(They cut corn. They start to yawn but Hen makes them continue)* Carry on!

They grind the corn, make the dough, put bread in the oven and take it out – clock and/or sign to indicate 30 minutes passing as before

Hen:	And here it is!
All animals:	If you work hard, you can eat the bread! *(They all look proud of their bread)*

The End

Poor Father Christmas (Pauvre Papa Noël)

Scene 1

At Father Christmas' house
Girl on stage in background to the side, Elves and Father Christmas in centre. Christmas tree to other side with Fairy unmoving on top

Elf 1:	Father Christmas, wake up. The letters have arrived!
Father Christmas:	*(Very grumpy)* Already! What's the date today?
Elf 1:	It's the 24th December!
Father Christmas:	The 24th December! Oh my Goodness. Better start then *(Very grumpy, picks up letters randomly)* ... Canada ... Australia ... Japan *(discards these)* ... France! *(Opens letter)*
Girl:	*(Starts reading aloud her version of the letter as she writes it, Father Christmas reads his version of the letter as she writes)*
	Dear Father Christmas. How are you? I can't wait 'til Christmas. May I have a teddy bear for my sister, a rabbit for my brother and some pencils for me please?

Girl seals and posts letter then goes off stage quietly

Father Christmas:	What a nice letter. OK, a teddy bear, a rabbit and some pencils. Here they are. *(Puts items in sack)* Rudolf ... where are you?

Rodolf limps in with crutches

Rudolf:	*(Crossly)* Yes.
Father Christmas:	It's 9:30, get the sleigh ready!
Rudolf:	I can't ... . I've got a bad leg.
Father Christmas:	Bother! What are we going to do?
Elf 2:	Hurry up, Father Christmas, it's nearly 10:00.
Father Christmas:	Can you help?
Elf 2:	Me? Sorry, I've got a headache. *(Sits by the fire)*
Father Christmas:	Bad leg ... headache. *(Mutters grumpily to himself whilst preparing sack)* And now it's snowing! *(Opens door, sees snow and stomps down the street with his sack to find reindeer)*
	Reindeer! *(Calls Reindeer to him, they rush over excitedly)*
Reindeer 1:	Hello Father Christmas ... where are the pizzas?
All the reindeer:	I'm hungry, I'm hungry.
Father Christmas:	Pizzas? No! We have to get ready ... it's Christmas Day tomorrow!
Reindeer 1:	I've got earache.
Father Christmas:	*(Muttering crossly)* Earache. Oh dear ... . *(To all the other Reindeer)* Will you help me?

Reindeer 2:	No, it's too cold.
Reindeer 3:	No, I've got a sore throat.
Reindeer 4:	No, I don't like the snow.
Reindeer 5:	No, I don't like children!

Father Christmas goes sadly back down the street to home, sits by the fire with Elves and looks weary

Father Christmas: What are we going to do? *(Elves look very sympathetic)*

Fairy climbs down quietly from tree, creeps behind Father Christmas and Elves and knocks on the door

Fairy: Knock, knock, knock!

Father Christmas opens the door grumpily, then pleased to see Fairy

Father Christmas: Oh! Hello! *(Kisses on both cheeks)*

Elf 2:   She is really beautiful! *(Acts as if he really likes her)*

Fairy: *(To Elf 2)* Stop! *(Pushing him lightly away, good humouredly)*
Father Christmas, the children are expecting their presents. What's going on?

Father Christmas: The reindeer are all ill ... bad legs ... earache ... .

Freeze-frame of all Reindeer, including Rudolf, looking cold, ill, etc

Fairy: You just need a little magic! Pouf! *(She zaps them and they jump up)*

All reindeer: Let's get to work! *(They line up in front of Fairy and salute her, then get busy, they march off stage, but Rudolf goes in wrong direction, they call him back)* Rudolf! *(He runs back and joins on their line. They bring sledge on for Father Christmas)*

Rudolf: Here it is!

Father Christmas: Thank you very much! *(Off he goes with bag, dropping presents at houses)*

Pupil comes on with a sign '25th December'. Girl wakes up next day and finds her presents, excitedly grabbing pencils

Girl: Ahh ... pencils ... . Thank you Father Christmas!

Father Christmas gives her a cheery wave

The End

Goldilocks (Boucle d'Or)

Scene 1

At Goldilocks's house
Goldilocks on stage admiring herself and flicking her hair, Mum and Sister on stage too

Goldilocks:	I am <u>so</u> beautiful!
	Mum, I'm hungry! What is there to eat?
Mum:	Potatoes, peas, carrots and mushrooms.
	Mmmm, it's very good! *(Mum looks enthusiastic!)*
Goldilocks:	Yes, it's very good ... *(as an aside to the audience only)* for your health!
Sister:	*(In 'goody-two-shoes' voice)* Thanks Mum, I love vegetables. *(Mum pleased with her)*
Goldilocks:	*(In a huff)* I'm going for a walk.
Sister:	Can I come?
Goldilocks:	No! *(Goes off skipping and singing in the woods, then off stage)*
	Alouette, gentille alouette, alouette, je te plumerai ... .

Scene 2

At the Three Bears' house

Baby Bear:	Hello Mummy! Can we do some cooking together?
Mummy Bear:	Yes, of course. I am going to make soup.
Baby Bear:	Soup? Onion soup?! *(Looks disappointed, then cross!)*
Mummy Bear:	No, no ... honey soup! *(Holds up large honey pot)*
Baby Bear:	Mmm! Delicious! What shall we put in the soup?

Baby Bear repeats each item as Mummy Bear adds them to the pot, then stirs

Mummy Bear:	Milk.
Baby Bear:	Milk.
Mummy Bear:	Sugar.
Baby Bear:	Sugar.
Mummy Bear:	And honey.
Baby Bear:	And honey.

Daddy Bear arrives

Daddy Bear:	Hello little one. *(Kisses Baby Bear on top of head)*
	Hello dear. *(Kisses Mummy Bear on each cheek as she is pouring three bowls of soup)*
	Mmm, it smells good! *(Tries to taste soup, but Mummy Bear stops him, lightly smacking his hand)*

Mummy Bear:	No, you have to wait. We are going for a walk.

All the Bears go off for a walk then off stage. Mice come out of hiding

Mouse 1:	Mmm, honey soup. It smells good. I am very hungry.
Mouse 2:	Can we? Oh no, I dare not!

Scene 3

In the woods
Goldilocks comes back across the stage

Goldilocks:	*(Singing last part of Alouette)* Je te plumerai le bec,
	Je te plumerai le bec,
	Et le bec, et le bec,
	Alouette, alouette.

Goldilicks starts to feel nervous, looks all around her and walks backwards into Red Riding Hood

Red Riding Hood:	*(Dancing and singing)* Sur le pont d'Avignon *(Bumps into Goldilocks. They both jump and look scared, then are pleased to see each other*
Red Riding Hood:	Goldilocks!
Goldilocks:	Red Riding Hood! *(French kisses – four on cheeks)* Where are you going?
Red Riding Hood:	I'm going to my Grandma's house. We're going to have a picnic.
Goldilocks:	What's in your basket?
Red Riding Hood:	Apples, lemonade and cakes.
Goldilocks:	It smells good, can I try it?
Red Riding Hood:	No, it's for my Grandma! *(Little Red Riding Hood pulls basket away crossly and goes off)*

Scene 4

In woods
Giant arrives taking big heavy steps, then sniffs; Goldilocks, frightened, tries to hide

Giant:	Fi fi fo fum ... *(sniffs)* I smell the blood of an Englishman.
Goldilocks:	*(Indignantly)* No, an English girl!
Giant:	I'm hungry. I'm going to eat you.

Giant starts to move towards Goldilocks; she faces up to him and steps forward

Goldilocks:	Go and eat carrots. *(Giant steps back as she steps forward)*
Giant:	Carrots! I'm not a vegetarian! I am French!
	(Holds hand over heart in honour pose, facing the audience)
	I want to eat beef or sausages or little girls! *(Steps forward again towards Goldilocks and rubs his tummy. She steps back)*

Goldilocks gasps crossly, sticks her tongue out and scares Giant. He stomps off muttering. Goldilocks runs to Three Bears' house, gingerly opens door and sees bowls on table

Scene 5

At the Three Bears' house
Goldilocks is on stage. Mice hiding to one side

Goldilocks:	Mmm, what's this? Soup? Honey soup? *(She tries the three bowls)* It's too cold ... *(short pause)* it's too hot ... *(short pause)* it's just right! I'll eat the lot! *(Eats up smallest bowl)* I'm sleepy. *(Yawns, and lies down on a cushion)*

Bears return home but mice don't realise at first

Mouse 1:	Is she asleep?
Mouse 2:	Yes, let's eat! *(They eat from Mummy Bear and Daddy Bear's bowls, but don't finish them)* Help! *(Mice see Bears, look scared and hide)*

Scene 6

Bears look at their soup bowls

Mummy Bear:	Who's been eating my soup?
Daddy Bear:	Who's been eating my soup?
Baby Bear:	*(Cries)* Who's been eating my soup and now it's all gone?

Mummy Bear and Daddy Bear comfort Baby Bear patting him/her on head

Mummy Bear:	Don't worry little one. We can make more soup ... .

Baby Bear spots Goldilocks asleep

Baby Bear:	Look! Who are you?
Mummy Bear:	Who are you?
Daddy Bear:	Who are you?
Mummy Bear:	Have you been eating my soup?
Daddy Bear:	Have you been eating my soup?
Baby Bear:	Have you eaten all my soup?
Goldilocks:	*(Goldilocks wakes up and looks scared)* Yes ... I'm sorry ... I'm frightened. Help!

Bears roar at her one after the other and lean over with claws out. They need to freeze-frame this pose and hold it for a few minutes. Red Riding Hood arrives with Grandma, sister, Woodcutter and Lulu (a dog)

Red Riding Hood:	Shall we eat here Grandma? *(Spreads picnic cloth on ground)*
Grandma:	Yes, this is a good place to eat.
Woodcutter:	It's a beautiful spot. I'm hungry. What's for lunch?

Lulu:	Woof! Woof! *(Tries to get them to see the Bears)*
Grandma:	Stop it, Lulu! Sit!
	Oh dear! Look – it's Goldilocks! *(Grandma shocked to see Goldilocks threatened by Bears – all still in frozen pose)*
Woodcutter:	No, no, don't kill her!
Sister:	Nobody hurts my sister!
Red Riding Hood:	Sit down. We are going to have a teddy bears' picnic! *(Takes each Bear by the hand and sits them down gently. Gets out cakes, lemonade, and honey)*
Red Riding Hood:	Here we are! Cakes, lemonade, honey.
Lulu:	And red wine! *(Passes red wine to Grandma who immediately takes a swig)*
Grandma:	It's very good … hic! *(Getting tipsy)*
Three Bears:	Mmm, it looks so good.

They all sit down and look happy, teddy bears' picnic music plays in background, the Bears, Woodcutter, Lulu and Grandma eat and gradually drift off to sleep, Grandma a bit tipsy

Red Riding Hood:	Come on! *(The girls creep away and high five each other over the top of the group as they go)*

The End

Rapunzel and the Eiffel Tower (Rapunzel et la tour Eiffel)

Scene 1

Paris

Rapunzel leaning out of her window of the Eiffel Tower, other characters come on and introduce themselves, without even noticing her

Rapunzel:	I'm Rapunzel. *(Waves from her window)*
Cinderella:	I'm Cinderella. *(Leans on her broom)*
Alice:	I'm Alice. *(Curtsies)*
Rumplestiltskin:	I'm Rumplestiltskin. *(Waves to audience)*
Prince:	I'm Prince Charming. *(Takes off hat and bows extravagantly)*

White Rabbit runs on

White Rabbit:	*(Panting)* I'm the White Rabbit and I'm late. *(Runs off, looking at watch)*
Everyone:	We're on holiday in Paris!

They pose, White Rabbit runs back on and takes a photo quickly, they all leave quietly, Witch comes on but they don't see her

Witch:	And I'm the Witch. *(Sweeps her cloak around her dramatically. Only Rapunzel notices her)*
Rapunzel:	Mum! *(Waves to Witch)*
Witch:	*(Waves back pretending to be nice and says as an aside to the audience and laughs)* I'm not really her Mum.

Scene 2

Rapunzel's room in the Eiffel Tower
Rapunzel sitting by window brushing hair

Rapunzel:	Today's my birthday and I'm 16 years old ... *(pauses)* but, I'm all alone. *(Looks sad)* I've got an idea! *(Suddenly looks pleased as she has the idea of writing a list of qualities she wants in a friend. Talks as she writes on several pieces of paper)*
Rapunzel:	Wanted: friend for young girl ... who lives ... no, who is a <u>prisoner</u> in the Eiffel Tower. Must be ... *(pauses to think)* ... nice ... charming ... strong ... chatty ... . And? Sporty, yes, sporty. *(Picks up notes)*
Witch:	Rapunzel! *(Calls out, then comes in holding cake)*

Rapunzel hides notes behind back, then throws them out of the window rather than let the Witch see them

Witch:	Happy Birthday, Rapunzel. *(Kisses on both cheeks, gives birthday cake)*
Rapunzel:	Thank you ... . A cake for me! *(She is pleased at first, then realises it is green. Says disgustedly)* Euh ... is it a salad cake?!
Witch:	Yes, it's very good for ... for ... for your hair!
Rapunzel:	My hair! *(Indignantly)* I've already got very long hair, Mum!

Rapunzel then looks out of window and lets hair fall out

Witch:	I know! I'm going to the market, goodbye.

Witch starts to climb down hair, Rapunzel groans as she pulls on her hair. Then Witch sticks head back through window, giving Rapunzel a fright

Witch:	Don't go out Rapunzel ... it's dangerous!

Witch goes off stage

Rapunzel:	Dangerous! That's ridiculous. I'm going to make a chocolate cake. *(Drops green cake in bin. Crossly gets bowl and puts ingredients in: sugar cubes, butter in packet, chocolate eggs still in foil!)* Sugar, butter, eggs.

Scene 3

Outside the Eiffel Tower
Other characters arrive by taxi and gather as tourists, taking photos and admiring the tower

Prince:	Here is the Eiffel Tower!
Alice:	It's amazing!
Rumplestiltskin:	It's very tall ... . Three hundred metres ... wow!
White Rabbit:	Shall we go up?
Rumplestiltskin:	Yes ... er ... shall we take the lift? *(Points to picture of a lift)*

Goes over to lift and takes no entry sign off, then reads notice out loud

Rumplestiltskin:	No entry. Out of order ... for 16 years! Bother!

All characters look shocked and look at each other in disbelief

Everyone:	16 years. Bother!

Cinderella notices pieces of paper on floor

Cinderella:	What's this? *(Picks them up and starts to read them)* Young girl ... 16 years old ... would like to make friends ... . <u>Prisoner</u> in the Eiffel Tower.
Everyone:	<u>Prisoner</u>? *(All characters gasp and look up ... Cinderella reads on)*
Cinderella:	... would prefer them to be ... nice ... *(pauses)* nice? I'm nice! *(She looks pleased. Rumplestiltskin, White Rabbit and Prince*

agree with a nod, but Alice has other ideas!)

Alice:	No! <u>I'm</u> nice! *(Takes papers from Cinderella, who then sadly picks up a broom and starts sweeping. Meanwhile Alice continues reading notes)* Sporty ... .
White Rabbit:	I'm sporty. *(He runs on the spot and does press-ups or he picks up taxi and runs off with it. Alice is impressed)*
Alice:	*(Still reading notes)* Charming ... .
Prince:	I'm very charming. *(Bows to Cinderella, takes broom from her and starts sweeping. Cinderella looks dreamily at him, like she might fall in love with him!)*
Cinderella:	He is nice!
White Rabbit:	This is ridiculous! *(Cinderella swoons over Prince; White Rabbit tuts impatiently)*
Alice:	*(Continues reading notes)* Chatty ... .
Rumplestiltskin:	I'm chatty! Blah, blah, blah, blah ... . *(Others cover their ears)*
Alice:	*(Still reading)* And strong!
Prince:	I'm strong! *(He flexes his muscles, then picks up the Eiffel Tower. Cinderella is impressed)*

Rapunzel stumbles across her moving floor, then yells out the window to him

Rapunzel:	Stop! *(Prince puts tower down and White Rabbit talks crossly to him)*
White Rabbit:	*(Impatiently taps watch)* Excuse-me ... . *(Crossly)* I'm late. Are we going up or not?
Everyone:	*(Excitedly because they want to meet Rapunzel)* Yes, let's go and see Rapunzel!
White Rabbit:	Shall we take the stairs? *(Limbers up, ready to climb stairs)*
Everyone:	Yes ... *(keen at first, then look up at height of tower and change minds)* or maybe not!

They all move to face audience in a line to give their excuses

Rumplestiltskin:	I'm too small.
Alice:	Me too. I'm too small. No, too big ... too small ... too big ... . *(Makes herself small, big, small, big as in Wonderland story. She could pretend to take a swig from a potion bottle between each phrase)*
White Rabbit:	This is ridiculous! Let's go ... ! *(He starts to run upstairs)* 1, 2, 3, 4, 5, 6, 7, 8, 9, 10 ... *(runs and puffs)* 20 ... *(puffs some more)* 50 ... oh, no ... it's too much ... . *(Sits exhausted, Alice comforts him)*
Prince:	Allow me. *(Shouts to Rapunzel)* Rapunzel ... Rapunzel ... let down your hair.

Hair comes falling down. Prince climbs up, then he goes down on one knee and opens ring box

Prince:	Rapunzel, will you marry me?
Rapunzel:	Oh, that was quick! But no! *(She is surprised then shakes her head)*

Alice and Cinderella climb up hair next. Prince proposes to both

Prince:	*(To Alice)* Will you marry me!
Alice:	Err ... No!
Prince:	*(To Cinderella)* Will you marry me?
Cinderella:	*(She is tempted!)* Maybe ... . *(Alice pulls her away)*
Alice:	No!

Prince looks annoyed but then hears someone climbing up and listens with interest, ready to propose again! Rumplestiltskin climbs up and Prince hastily changes his mind

Prince:	Marry ... er no ... .

Rumplestiltskin sees ring box and snatches it off him then throws it over his shoulder. White Rabbit catches box and climbs up then tries to propose to Prince Charming!

White Rabbit:	Will you marry me? *(Prince looks really annoyed!)*

Rapunzel excitedly greets her new friends

Alice:	I'm Alice. *(Curtsies and smiles)*
Rapunzel:	Pleased to meet you. *(Shakes hands)*
Cinderella:	I'm Cinderella. *(Curtsies and smiles)*
Rapunzel:	Pleased to meet you. *(Shakes hands)*
Rumpletstiltskin:	I'm Rumplestiltskin. *(He bows)*
Rapunzel:	Pleased to meet you. *(Shakes hands)*
White Rabbit:	I'm ... *(not sure of his own name)* I'm the white rabbit.
Rapunzel:	Pleased to meet you. *(Shakes hands)*

Girls start to make friends

Cinderella:	Your hair is beautiful! *(Admires Rapunzel's hair)*
Alice:	Your dress is beautiful. *(Admires her dress)*
Rapunzel:	I've got friends! I'm so happy.

Rapunzel links arms with new friends, they go off and find the cake. Prince sulks in the corner. White Rabbit and Rumplestiltskin try to comfort him

Rumplestiltskin:	Blah, blah blah, blah ... . *(Not too loudly)*

All girls come back, bringing cake in

Alice and Cinderella:	Mmm, it smells good.
Prince:	Sit down everyone. Let's eat. *(Cheers up at arrival of the cake)*

Everyone sits down, Rapunzel at window. Witch appears outside at the bottom of the Eiffel Tower and wants to come up

Witch:	Rapunzel, Rapunzel, let down your hair. I want to come up.
Rapunzel:	It's Mum! *(Rapunzel looks annoyed and lets down her hair impatiently)*
White Rabbit:	No, she's a witch !
Rapunzel:	Huh! *(Gasps as she realises the Witch isn't her Mum)* She's not my Mum?
White Rabbit:	No.
Rapunzel:	Fantastic! *(Very pleased ... pauses)* So ... cut off my hair! *(Decisively)*
Cinderella:	Cut off your hair? *(Looks worried and upset)*
Prince:	Allow me! *(Flexes his muscles, and poses like a body builder. Mimes scissors with fingers)*

Rabbit comes up behind him, pulls the wig off Rapunzel and lets it fall

White Rabbit:	Done! *(Prince looks really cross with White Rabbit)*
Rapunzel:	My hair!

Rapunzel looks down from window. Witch falls and hobbles off clutching her bottom

Witch:	Ow ... my bottom!
Rapunzel:	Phew!
Rumplestiltskin:	Let's have some cake! *(Cuts the cake and gives everyone a piece)*
Everyone:	Happy Birthday, Rapunzel, Happy Birthday!

The end

Puss in Boots (Le Chat Botté)

Scene 1

At the family farm
Father and sons all working together. Father calls/whistles for them to stop and they gather together

Father:	My sons ... I am getting old.
All sons:	Oh no, Dad!
Father:	Yes, I am ... and I am tired. You will need to work more on the farm.
All:	Yes, Dad.
Father:	John, I give you ... my windmill. *(Gives him windmill)*
John:	*(Looks pleased)* It's super. Thanks Dad.
Father:	Luke, I give you ... my horse.
Luke:	*(Looks pleased)* He is wonderful. Thank you Dad.
Father:	Mark, I give you ... my cat.
Mark:	*(A bit disappointed)* Your cat? Thanks, Dad.
Puss in Boots:	Meow.
Father:	Work hard my sons.
John:	Sit down, Dad. *(Gets Dad to sit down)*
All:	Let's get to work. Bye Dad. *(They limber up enthusiastically and get ready for work)*

Scene 2

Outside
Brothers are discussing and admiring their gifts

Mark:	So, you get the mill, you get the horse ... *(older two look proudly at their gifts)* and me ... I get the cat!
Puss in Boots:	Meow! *(Other brothers go, Puss in Boots nuzzles up to Mark)*
Mark:	You are a very kind little cat. *(Strokes Puss in Boots)* But we are going to be poor ... very poor. *(In despair, sobs)*
Puss in Boots:	Meow. Listen to me.
Mark:	*(Gasps as he hears Puss in Boots speak)* Huh! You can talk!
Puss in Boots:	Yes ... work hard and you will be rich.
Mark:	Rich ... that's not possible!
Puss in Boots:	Yes it is. Listen to me. First, I would like a bag and some boots.
Mark:	Boots? *(Mark moves off to get them and Puss in Boots keeps shouting for more things as he goes)*
Puss in Boots:	Yes, and a hat ... a jacket ... trousers.

Mark:	Here they are.
Puss in Boots:	Thank you. *(Gets dressed, admiring himself, arranges hat, smooths out whiskers)*
	It really suits me! *(To Mark)* Master, let's get to work.

Scene 3

In the fields

Mark works hard in the fields all day long, looks tired. Someone holds up a clock with hands whirring round to show the day progressing. Mark starts to walk home with vegetables he has collected, singing as he goes. Suddenly he spots John sleeping beside his windmill, which is going too fast (someone needs to blow the beach windmill quite fast!) Mark stops beside brother, then sings louder and faster to wake his brother up.

Mark:	*(Gentle at first, getting louder)*
	Meunier, tu dors? Ton moulin, ton moulin va trop vite
	Meunier, tu dors? Ton moulin, ton moulin va trop fort
	Ton moulin, ton moulin va trop vite
	Ton moulin, ton moulin va trop fort *(Repeats last two lines singing faster, jumping up and down and shouting)*

Brother John wakes up suddenly and Mark helps him stop the windmill

| John: | Thank you brother. |

Mark walks on and sees his other brother Luke further on down the road, singing as if drunk. Luke catches hold of Mark and forces Mark to dance with him

Luke:	*(Singing)* Sur le pont d'Avignon,
	On y danse, on y danse
	Sur le pont d'Avignon,
	On y danse tous en rond.
Mark:	*(A bit crossly)* Stop it! Where is the horse?
Luke:	I don't know. *(Shrugs, shakes head and holds hands out)*

Mark goes off to find horse

| Luke: | *(Falls in a sleepy heap on the floor, then hiccups)* Hiccup! |

Mark finds horse who looks worried

Mark:	*(To horse)* There you are. Are you OK?
Horse:	Neigh, neigh. I've got a headache. *(Holds hands over ears)*
Mark:	You can talk too! Come on. *(Leads horse home)*
	You'll be OK here. Have a rest. *(Lets him rest and eat grass)*

Puss in Boots returns and sees vegetables then quickly arranges them in a basket

| Puss in Boots: | *(Seizes basket)* Excellent. You have been working hard. |
| Mark: | But, that's my dinner! |

Scene 4

At the King's castle
Puss in Boots goes off with basket of food singing. Someone holds up sign for 'Monday.' Puss in Boots arrives at King's castle and knocks on the door

Puss in Boots:	*(Singing)* Lundi matin, l'empereur, sa femme et le petit Prince sont venus chez moi pour me serrer la pince … . Knock, knock, knock.
King:	Yes … oh, hello! *(Surprised to see a cat!)*
Puss in Boots:	A present from my master: 'Mark de Carabas'! *(Says name of master proudly)*
King:	Thank you very much. *(Takes basket the cat offers)*

Someone holds up sign for 'Tuesday'. Puss in Boots goes off stage and back on again quickly, with basket of fruit

Puss in Boots:	*(Singing)* Mardi matin, l'empereur, sa femme et le petit Prince sont venus chez moi pour me serrer la pince … . Knock, knock. knock.
King:	Yes … hello. *(Pleased to see cat again)*
Puss in Boots:	A present from my master: 'Mark de Carabas'.
King:	Thank you very much.

Someone holds up sign for 'Wednesday'. Puss in Boots off stage and back on again quickly with a basket of soft toys so that he looks like a good hunter

Puss in Boots:	*(Singing)* Mercredi matin, l'empereur, sa femme et le petit Prince sont venus chez moi pour me serrer la pince … . Knock, knock, knock.
King:	Yes, hello … Mr Cat.
Puss in Boots:	A present from my master: 'Mark de Carabas'.
King:	Thank you … your master is very generous. Wait. *(Asks Puss in Boots inside)*
King:	*(Calls out quietly, becoming louder)* Princesses … Princesses … Princesses!

Princess arrives with sisters and white cat

Princess:	Yes, Father.
White cat:	Meow! *(Looks at Puss in Boots with interest!)*
Puss in Boots:	Meow! *(Makes purring sounds)*
Sister 1:	Look at the cats. *(Nudges sister to look at cats)*
Sister 2:	Look at the mice. *(Nudges sister to look at mice)*

Mice saunter into room, singing

Mice:	Alouette, gentille alouette ... .
	Alouette, je te plumerai!

Then the mice see Puss in Boots, gasp and hide behind the chair

Mouse:	Sshh, it's Puss in Boots!
Princess:	(Beckons Puss in Boots over) Mr Cat ... I have a problem: my cat will not chase mice!

White cat goes over to mice and purrs at them. Puss in Boots rolls his eyes and shakes his head/finger at other cat

King:	I've got an idea. You are a very good hunter. Stay here.

Puss in Boots thinks, nods to the King and shows his claws to the mice who run off stage. He is tempted by offer but hesitates

Puss in Boots:	It's a good idea ... but first, I must talk it over with my master.
King:	Alright. Come along girls ... let's go for a walk.
Princesses:	(They salute their father) Yes Father.

Puss in Boots runs back to farm – across stage a couple of times – King and princesses walk slowly

Scene 5

At the farm
The three brothers and Dad are singing "Frère Jacques" (normal version) and enjoying each other's company

Brothers and Dad:	Frère Jacques, Frère Jacques.
	Dormez–vous ? Dormez–vous ?

Puss in Boots arrives and stops them, pulling Mark away

Puss in Boots:	Stop! Come quickly, the King is passing by.

Mark hastily jumps on horse and they rush to the river

Scene 6

At the river

Puss in Boots:	Here's the river ... . Swim!
Mark:	Swim? (Puss in Boots nods) What about my clothes!
Puss in Boots:	Take them off!
Mark:	Take them off?!
Puss in Boots:	Yes!

Mark goes reluctantly behind screen, chucks a spare hat and socks over screen as if he has just taken them off and pretends to swim. Then the King and daughters arrive. Princess admires horse

Princess:	Look at the horse.
Sister 1:	Do you like horse-riding?
Princess:	Yes, I love it. What about you?
Sister 1:	I prefer walking.
Sister 2:	And I like swimming! *(Looks with interest at Mark swimming in water)*
Princess:	*(To horse, stroking him)* You are very handsome.

Horse neighs

King:	Oh, hello, Mister Cat.
Puss in Boots:	Hello, Your Majesty ... *(Puss in Boots tries to kiss King's hand, but King snatches it away)*
	This is Mark de Carabas. *(Puss in Boots points at Mark swimming. Sisters giggle and look interested!)*
King:	Pleased to meet you, Sir. *(King is delighted to meet Mark who stretches arm around screen to shake hands with him)*
Puss in Boots:	*(Explains Master's reluctance to appear)* He's lost his T-shirt ...
King:	Oh I understand ... take my jacket. *(King gives him his own jacket)*
Mark:	Thank you.
King:	Thank <u>you</u> for all the presents. Now, come to the castle. *(They all go back to castle)*
Sister 2:	Yes, come and eat with us. *(They continue walking and arrive at castle)*
Sister 1:	Here is the castle ... come in!
Mark:	It's fantastic!
King:	Sit down. *(King indicates for Mark to sit, but there is no chair, so he kneels)*

White cat comes in and stays close to Puss in Boots, they meow at each other

White cat:	How are you?
Puss in Boots:	Fine thanks, how about you?
White cat:	I'm very well ... now! *(White cat snuggles up to Puss in Boots)* Meow, meow, meow.

King decides to honour Mark, to his great surprise. He places a crown on Mark's head and touches both shoulders with his sword

King:	There you are! Now you're a real Prince.
Mark:	*(Looks surprised)* Thank you but ... I'd prefer to live with my brothers.

Mark gives crown back and waves to brothers in the distance, horse on stage too now

King:	Oh!
Princess:	How many brothers have you got?

Mark:	Two. What about you?
Princess:	I've got two sisters. *(Points to sisters who wave to the brothers excitedly)*
Sisters:	Hello, hello!

Princess stands with horse stroking him

Princess:	I love your horse … . *(Horse nuzzles up to her)*
King:	So, you're leaving? *(To Mark who nods)*
	What about you? *(To Puss in Boots)*
Puss in Boots:	I'd prefer to stay here. We can chase the mice.
White cat:	Yes, show me how to chase mice!

Puss in Boots beckons White cat over and mimes to her how to wait, get claws out and pounce … then she proposes!

White cat:	Thank you … marry me? *(Puss in Boots who is unsure, looks at the other characters questioningly, but they all nod to him)*
Everyone:	Say yes!
Puss in Boots:	Yes! *(They link arms and someone gives them flowers)*

Princess poses with horse, wearing a riding hat and rosette. One of the brothers takes a photo of her

King:	That's super. Thanks for everything, Mark. *(Shakes Mark's hand)*
	Let's have a party!
Mouse 1:	Can we sing Frère Jacques now?
Mouse 2:	Yes, let's do the Rock and Roll version!

The End

Snow White and the sporty dwarves (Blanche-Neige et les nains sportifs)

Scene 1

Snow White's home
Queen and Mirror on stage

Queen:	Mirror, Mirror, on the wall, who is the fairest of them all? *(Admires herself in the mirror)*
Mirror:	Not you! It's Snow White!
Queen:	*(Crossly)* Snow White! *(Then at the mirror, hoping for a positive response)*
	Mirror, Mirror, on the wall, who is the best dancer? *(Spins round)*
Mirror:	Not you! It's Snow White!
Queen:	*(More crossly!)* Snow White!
	Mirror, Mirror, on the wall, who is the best golf player? *(Mimes playing golf)*
Mirror:	Not you! It's Snow White!
Queen:	Snow White! *(Furious now!)*
	Where is my husband? *(Calls out increasingly loud and cross)* Dracula.

Dracula arrives and sweeps his cloak around himself dramatically looking at the audience

Queen:	We're going to play golf!
Dracula:	Yes dear. *(Goes off with queen as a dutiful husband)*

Scene 2

At the golf club
Snow White plays a winning shot and all club members cheer!

Everyone:	Hurray! Snow White has won.

Club President crowns Snow White / gives her cup

President:	Congratulations Snow White. The golf champion!
Everybody:	Hurray, hurray.

Queen arrives

Queen:	Champion? You stupid girl! Go! *(Waves Snow White off the stage.)* And don't come back! *(Queen goes off stage, looking pleased to be rid of Snow White)*

Scene 3

In the woods. The Dwarves' cottage is to one side
Snow White wanders back on to stage as if walking through the woods, looking worried

Snow White:	*(To the audience)* What am I going to do?
	(Carries on wandering and finds the cottage)
	What a pretty house ... . *(Knocks on the door)*
	Is there anybody home? *(Goes in and looks around and touches all the objects eg radio TV)*
	This is great. I can listen to the radio ... play the piano ... watch TV ... . *(Sits down, then leaps up)*
	No, I am going to work. *(Sweeps the floor, and starts cooking, sings to herself)* Alouette, gentille alouette.
	Alouette, je te plumerai ... .
	Dinner ... . Mmm it smells good! *(Puts ingredients in and stirs pot)*

The Seven Dwarves come home from work

All the Dwarves:	*(Singing)* Sur le pont d'Avignon, on y danse, on y danse
	Sur le pont d'Avignon, on y danse, tous en rond.

As they get to the cottage and see door open, they are worried and stop abruptly, crashing into each other

Dwarves:	*(Each one turns round and says to the one behind)* Watch it! *(The last one – Dwarf 7, does this too, even though there is no one behind him/her)*

They go through the door, see Snow White, gasp and look frightened

Dwarf 1:	Who are you?
Snow White:	I'm Snow White, and you?

Each dwarf introduces himself and mimes his or her activity. They all stand in a line facing the audience.

Dwarf 1:	I'm Swimmer dwarf. *(Mimes swimming)*
Snow White:	Pleased to meet you! *(Moves along line kissing each on the forehead, they look pleased but embarrassed!)*
Dwarf 2:	I'm Footballer dwarf. *(Mimes kicking ball)*
Snow White:	Pleased to meet you!
Dwarf 3:	I'm Dancing dwarf. *(Mimes dancing)*
Snow White:	Pleased to meet you!
Dwarf 4:	I'm Tennis dwarf. *(Mimes playing tennis)*
Snow White:	Pleased to meet you!
Dwarf 5:	I'm Gymnastic dwarf *(Mimes gymnastic moves)*
Snow White:	Pleased to meet you!
Dwarf 6:	I'm Singing dwarf *(Sings)*
Snow White:	Pleased to meet you!

Dwarf 7:	I'm Sleepy Dwarf *(Yawns)*
Snow White:	Pleased to meet you!
Dwarf 1:	You've been working hard! *(Looks around at the clean house)*
Dwarf 2:	The house is so clean.
Dwarf 3:	Mmm, something smells good. *(Smells the lovely food cooking in the pot)*
Dwarf 4:	I'm hungry!

All the dwarves try to sit down to eat, looking hopeful, but Snow White sends them off

Snow White:	No, first you have to work!
	(To dwarf 5) What job will you do?
Dwarf 5:	I will do some gardening. *(Pretends to dig the garden)*
Snow White:	And you?
Dwarf 6:	I will do some sweeping. *(Pretends to sweep with a broom)*
Snow White:	And you?
Dwarf 7:	I will do some cleaning. *(Pretends to clean and dust)*
Snow White:	And you?
Dwarf 1:	I will make the beds. *(Makes the beds)*
Snow White:	And you?
Dwarf 2:	I will lay the table *(Lays the table)*
Snow White:	And you?
Dwarf 3:	I will do some DIY *(Pretends to fix shelves)*
Snow White:	And you?
Dwarf 4:	I will do some knitting. *(Gets out knitting)*

They all work for a few seconds

Snow White:	Dinner's ready. *(Calls them to eat, they come and sit down)*
All the Dwarves:	It smells good! Delicious!

They all eat, then Snow White asks each of them about their hobbies

Snow White:	What do you do in your spare time?
Dwarf 1:	I like reading
Snow White:	And you?
Dwarf 2:	I like playing cards.
Snow White:	And you?
Dwarf 3:	I like music.
Snow White:	And you?
Dwarf 4:	I like the cinema.
Snow White:	And you?
Dwarf 5:	I like the theatre.
Dwarf 6:	What about you, Snow White, what do you like doing?
Snow White:	I like playing the piano, cooking and playing golf!

All Dwarves:	*(Looking pleased)* Playing golf – that's great!
Snow White:	And you?
Dwarf 7:	I like sleeping! *(Pretends to sleep)*
All other dwarves:	Me too *(They pretend to sleep too)*

Snow White blows them all a kiss goodnight. Then Old Lady knocks at the door with an apple, Snow White opens the door and looks surprised

Old Lady:	An apple, Miss?
Snow White:	Yes, I love apples. *(Takes a bite and falls asleep, Old Lady goes off cackling)*

Dwarves wake up slowly and look upset when they see Snow White lying down, apparently unconscious

Dwarf 1:	Snow White!
Dwarf 2:	She must be tired.
Dwarves:	Yes. *(All nod, looking concerned)*
Dwarf 3:	She's been working too hard.
Dwarves:	Yes. *(All nod again)*
Dwarf 4:	She's been doing too much sport!
Dwarves:	Yes. *(All nod again)*
Dwarf 7:	She's been watching too much TV.
All:	Yes … . *(They all nod in agreement, then look crossly at Dwarf 7)* No!
Dwarf 6:	Look – the apple. *(He smells it and makes a face. They all gasp and start running around in a panic bumping into each other, then sit in a curve around Snow White, on knees praying*

Prince arrives riding his horse. He is lost and knocks on door. Dwarf 6 answers door

Prince:	I'm lost. Where's the sports centre, please?
Dwarf 6:	It's over there. *(Points to the distance but won't let the Prince leave)* But, wait, are you a prince?
Prince:	Yes. I am a prince. *(Proudly)*
Dwarf 5:	Then … you must kiss the girl. *(Tries to get Prince to kiss Snow White)*
Prince:	Kiss the girl? Absolutely not! But … she is pretty … she is charming … . *(He starts to change his mind, pacing back and forth, glancing at Snow White, Dwarves nod in agreement at what he says*
Prince:	Is she sporty?
All dwarves:	Yes, she's very sporty! *(Prince nods approvingly at each sport)*
Dwarf 4:	She plays volleyball.
Dwarf 3:	She plays basketball.
Dwarf 2:	She plays golf!

Dwarf 7:	She plays the piano. *(Prince looks confused at this)*
Prince:	Alright. I will kiss her. *(He kisses her and she wakes up and they look happy)*
Dwarves:	Is it love? Yes, yes, it is love!

The End

Wendy goes on holiday (Wendy part en vacances)

Scene 1

At Wendy's home in London

Wendy:	*(Talks to audience and excitedly jumps up and down, holds up air ticket)* Today I am going on holiday. I can't wait! ... Mum, where's my suitcase?
Mum:	Here it is!
Wendy:	OK, T-shirt, sunglasses, hat, alarm clock ... alarm clock? *(Looks puzzled at Mum)*
Mum:	*(Mum speaks strictly to Wendy and Wendy looks a bit worried)* Yes, the alarm will go off 30 minutes before the flight. Don't be late!

Taxi driver knocks at the door, Mum answers

Driver:	Taxi for the airport?
Mum:	Yes. Thank you ... Wendy, your taxi is here! Hurry up, the flight is at 5 o'clock.

Wendy jumps in taxi and goes off to airport

Scene 2

Waiting room of airport
Person sitting to the side at desk in box with frame of TV around them, getting increasingly sleepy until he/ she drops off. Wendy gives ticket in at check-in desk. Michael is sitting. Wendy fidgets, then decides to start a conversation, first moving into the seat next to Michael

Wendy:	I'm Wendy, who are you?
Michael:	I'm Michael. Where are you going?
Wendy:	I'm going to Spain, to sunbathe. How about you?
Michael:	I'm going to Italy. I'm going to visit the historical monuments.
Wendy:	That's interesting!

Lost Boy arrives with rucksack and map, looking lost

Wendy:	Hello. Where are you going?
Lost Boy:	I'm going camping and I'm looking for the station ... but I'm lost.
Wendy:	But this is the airport!
Lost Boy:	Yes, I know ... I'm a lost boy! *(He starts to cry loudly. Wendy comforts him)*

Mermaid arrives and boy stops crying. He and Michael look admiringly at her

Michael:	She is beautiful! *(To Lost Boy who nods in agreement)*
Wendy:	Where are you going?
Mermaid:	I'm going to Hawaii. I'm going to swim with the dolphins.
Lost Boy and Michael:	Great!

Indian arrives whooping, others look surprised but smile

Indian:	Hello, o, o, o, o! *(Hello stretches into whoop)*
	I'm going to Canada, to do some kayaking. *(Mimes kayaking)*
All:	Excellent! *(All characters clap)*

Fairy arrives flying on energetically and happily

Wendy:	Hello, where are you going ?
Fairy:	I'm going to New York to visit the museums ... *(others look impressed, then Fairy adds as an aside to the audience)* and do some shopping! *(Others wave fingers disapprovingly at 'shopping')*

Captain arrives dramatically with his crocodile and addresses the audience

Captain:	I am the Pirate Captain ... *(others look afraid)* and this is my crocodile!

Others, who are now friends run and hide behind chairs, then Indian comes cautiously out, taps Captain's shoulder and jumps back

Indian:	Excuse-me, where are you going?
Captain:	We are going ... . *(Looks thoughtful)*
All:	Yes ... . *(They look interested and start to come out)*
Captain:	We're going ... . *(Louder)*
All:	Yes? *(More interested and louder)*
Captain:	We're going ... . *(Very loud)*
All:	YES! *(Very loud)*
Captain:	To Blackpool! *(More quietly)*
All:	Blackpool! *(They look at him crossly)*
Captain:	Yes, we are going to dance and swim. *(Grabs crocodile and mimes dancing and swimming with him)*
Lost Boy:	You're going to dance with a crocodile?!
All:	Oh my Goodness! *(Make typical French gesture with hands)*

Alarm goes off

Wendy:	Oh no ! Half past four already! The flight! *(Tries to switch off alarm but it won't switch off)*
Captain:	Can I help?

Captain can't stop it either, so tosses it to Crocodile who swallows it!

Crocodile:	Mmm, it tastes good!
Wendy:	But ... my alarm clock! *(Looks cross, pauses, sits, then looks bored)* What shall we do? Watch TV?

Wendy switches TV on, person in box comes to life in the middle of weather forecast

Forecaster:	... and now we have the weather forecast for the holidays. *(Friends look interested and pleased, rub hands together)* It's raining. *(Friends look a bit disappointed and mime rain)* It's cold. *(Friends mime cold and look grumpy, thumbs down)* And there are tornadoes!
All:	Tornadoes! *(All look at each other frightened, jump up and down, run round in circles)*

Airport worker runs on with announcement

Airport worker:	Ladies and gentlemen, due to the bad weather, there are no more flights today!
All:	No more flights!

All stand up, look crossly at him and stick tongues out! He wags finger at them. Peter Pan arrives with a flourish; everyone looks surprised

Peter Pan:	I am Peter Pan. *(Stands proudly in a typical pose – hands on hips)*
Fairy and Mermaid:	Peter Pan! *(Pretend to feel faint)*
Lost Boy and Michael:	Ridiculous! *(They tut at girls)*
Peter Pan:	Don't worry, I can fly!

Peter Pan flies across stage, while the others sing

All:	You can fly, you can fly, Peter, you can fly!

Peter Pan grabs Wendy and she grabs Michael, they fly off, with Fairy and Mermaid too, around the stage

Captain:	Taxi!

Captain, Crocodile, Indian and Lost Boy rush off stage to catch taxi

Scene 3

Flying over holiday locations
Peter Pan, Wendy, Michael, Fairy and Mermaid fly over rooftops and countryside and look down at characters doing holiday activities

Wendy:	Look, that's London. There are lots of tourists, taking photos.
Michael:	And there's the campsite. They are playing volleyball and having a barbecue. *(All wave to campers)*
Peter Pan:	There's the beach. They are swimming and water-skiing. It's

	great! *(All wave)*
Wendy:	We're crossing the Channel. Look at the boats. And that's France! *(All wave)*
Mermaid:	That's Paris. They are visiting the Eiffel Tower and Notre Dame. *(All wave)*
Peter Pan:	Here we are! We have arrived ... at Disneyland!
All:	Disneyland! Cool!
Wendy:	I've dreamt of going to Disneyland all my life!

She jumps up and down excitedly, they all go off singing to the tune of 'Twinkle Twinkle Little Star'

All:	Magic is everywhere ... let the magic begin. *(x2)*

Someone shows sign saying 'One week later'

Scene 4

At Wendy's home in London
Wendy arrives home with Peter Pan, Fairy, Michael and Mermaid with souvenirs such as Disney Mickey ears.
TV presenter is falling asleep again

Wendy:	Knock, knock, knock.
Mum:	Wendy! *(Kisses both cheeks and hands Wendy postcard)*
Wendy:	Thank you. *(Glances at card and sits)*

Mum kisses all others except Peter Pan who refuses

Mum:	So, how was the holiday? Did you have a good time? *(All sit)*
Wendy:	Yes, we went to Disneyland. We played, danced, sang.
Mermaid:	We went on the ghost train.

Others pretend to be ghosts, Mermaid looks scared

Michael:	We watched the shows.
Fairy:	We bought souvenirs.
Peter Pan:	We ate ice-cream ... yum, yum.

Phone rings, Michael answers, Lost Boy at side of stage as if somewhere else

Michael:	Hello.
Lost Boy:	Hello ... Michael? How are you?
Michael:	I'm fine thanks. Where are you?
Lost Boy:	We're in Spain. We're camping. We took the train. It was really quick.
Michael:	Oh yes.
Lost Boy:	We've been sunbathing, swimming, fishing.
Michael:	Enjoy the rest of your holiday. Goodbye!
Lost Boy:	Goodbye.

Wendy's phone rings and she answers

Wendy:	Hello.
Indian:	Hello ... is that Wendy? Are you ok?
Wendy:	Yes thanks ... how was your holiday?
Indian:	I went to Switzerland by train. I went walking and canoeing.
Wendy:	Super ... . Thank you for the postcard. Goodbye!

All characters relax on sofa and decide to watch TV

Mermaid:	Shall we put the TV on?
All:	Yes! *(All enthusiastic; Mermaid switches on TV)*
Presenter:	And here is the news: Oh my Goodness! A crocodile has been found on the beach in Blackpool! All the tourists have gone!

All look scared and run off at mention of tourists leaving. Captain and Crocodile come on as if on beach. They relax back to back and waiter hands cocktails over their shoulders.

Captain:	Aren't holidays great!
All:	Yes, holidays are great!

The End

The three little pigs go to school (Les trois petits cochons vont à l'école)

Scene 1

At home

Dad and Mum:	Come here children! *(Pigs scurry in and stand to attention)*
Dad:	We have decided … *(parents pace up and down as they say each bit)*
Mum:	…. that it's time …
Dad:	… for you to leave home! *(Pigs look scared)*
Mum:	You are going to build your own houses!
Pigs:	Hooray! *(Excited … then worried)*
Pig 1:	But how?
Dad:	You're going to learn that at school!
Pigs:	Hooray … school? *(Enthusiastic, at first, then unsure)*
Mum:	Yes, you're going to learn maths … . *(Pigs all count on fingers, looking puzzled)*
Dad:	Music … . *(Pigs mime playing violins, recorders, guitars etc)*
Mum:	Sport … . *(Mime running and other sports)*
Dad:	And history.
Pigs:	Excellent! *(All clap and nod in agreement)*
Dad:	Work hard, but … watch out for wolves.
Pigs:	Wolves! *(They gasp and look scared)*
Mum:	Yes, they are everywhere!
Dad:	Goodbye children!

Three pigs leave home with rucksacks singing

Pigs:	Who's afraid of the big bad wolf?
	In any case, it's definitely not us! *(x2)*

Mum and Dad get out a bottle of wine and start relaxing

Dad:	Red wine dear?
Mum:	Thank you dear!

Scene 2

At school
Pigs arrive at 'Eat Everything School'

Pig 3:	'Eat Everything School', great!
Pig 1:	Check your bags. *(They stand to attention and hold up each item)*
	Ruler … pencil … rubber. Lets go!

Lesson 1: Maths
Pig 2 sees timetable posted and takes it down to read; the others look over his/her shoulder

Pig 2:	Here's the timetable. First lesson is maths.
Pig 3:	Maths? Oh no. That's difficult. I'm very bad at maths.
Maths teacher:	Good morning pigs, sit down. *(Holds up pictures of biscuits or plastic ones)* Now, 3 biscuits and 2 biscuits. How many is that altogether? *(Pigs think and count on fingers, then Pig 3 puts hand up, excitedly)*
Maths teacher:	Yes?
Pig 3:	None! We've eaten the lot! *(Others laugh)*
Maths teacher:	You fools! You are useless at maths. *(Pigs look ashamed and run off)*
Pig 1:	Oh my Goodness ... the teacher is strict!

Lesson 2: Music

Pig 1:	What lesson is it now?
Pig 2:	Music. I love music. It's my favourite subject. I hope that the teacher is nice.
Music teacher:	Hello everybody! Today we are going to sing!
Pig 2:	Hurray! I love singing!
Pigs:	La, la, la. *(All pigs sing really badly)*
Music teacher:	No, no, no! Listen and repeat. Do, Re, Mi, Fa, So, La, Ti, Do. *(Points to them in turn)*
Pig 1:	*(Sings well)* Do, Re, Mi, Fa, So, La, Ti, Do.
Pig 2:	*(Sings well)* Do, Re, Mi, Fa, So, La, Ti, Do.
Pig 3:	*(Sings badly)* So, Mi, Re, Do, Ti, Fa, Do. *(Other pigs stare at him)* I'm really bad at music.

Others look sympathetic and try to cheer Pig 3 up; he looks happier

Pig 1:	No you're not.
Music teacher:	Actually, you are really bad at music.
Pigs 1 and 2:	You're so mean! *(They look crossly at teacher!)*
Pig 3:	That teacher is strict.

Lesson 3: Sport

Pig 1:	What lesson is it now? *(They look at timetable)*
Pig 3:	Sport! I hope the teacher is fun.
Sports teacher:	Today we are going to play volleyball. *(Throws ball to pigs)*
Pig 2:	Great! I love playing volleyball. *(Bounces ball, others join in)*
Pig 1:	Is this right? *(To teacher, who shakes his head and looks cross)*
Pig 3:	I like sport. It's my favourite subject. *(Pigs mess about and pass ball to each other under their chins, through their legs etc.)*

Sports teacher:	Dear oh dear ... when does this lesson finish? *(Looks at watch in despair)*

Bell rings for break

Sports teacher:	Thank you! *(To the bell)*
Pigs:	It's break time!

Teachers all collapse in chairs in staff room, pigs go to play

Maths teacher:	Oh my Goodness ... those pigs.
Music teacher:	It's unbelievable ... they are so silly!
Sports teacher:	Yes, but think of the roast pork!

History teacher holds up picture of roast pork in thought bubble

All teachers:	Mmm, delicious!

Bell for end of break, pigs come back on stage

Pig 3:	What lesson is it now?
Pig 2:	History!
Pig 1:	Great! I love history! It's very interesting. I hope the teacher's nice.

Lesson 4: History

History teacher:	Today we are studying the English Kings. What can you tell me about Henry VIII? *(Holds up portrait of Henry VIII)*
Pig 2:	He had 6 wives. *(Looks at picture of Henry VIII's six wives; others look amazed)*
Pigs 1 and 3:	Six!
History teacher:	Yes. *(Teacher looks interested and pleased)*
Pig 1:	He was fat.
History teacher:	Yes. *(Teacher less pleased)*
Pig 3:	And he really liked eating ... *(hesitates as he/she tries to think)* chicken, fish and beef... . *(Teacher looking annoyed now)*
History teacher:	Yes ... and sausages! *(Pig 3 nods, Pigs 1 and 2 amazed at Pig 3 who doesn't get it)*
Pigs 1 and 2:	Sausages! *(Pig 3 looks confused)* Pigs! *(Pig 3 understands now and looks scared)*
Pig 3:	Aagh!

All teachers appear as wolves now

Pigs:	Wolves! Help!

They run off screaming, chased by wolves, then slow down to slow motion movement. Pig 1 stops the others

Pig 1:	Who's afraid of wolves?

Pigs pause

Pigs 2 and 3:	Not us!

Pigs turn around, paw at ground, then stick tongues out, scaring wolves off. Pigs collapse in heap on floor and look tired and relieved, then suddenly remember they haven't made their houses

Pigs:	The houses!

A few moments later they see the DIY teacher pass by

Pig 3:	Excuse me! Are you a teacher?
DIY teacher:	Yes.
Pig 2:	What subject?
DIY teacher:	DIY.
Pigs:	DIY! Perfect!
Pig 1:	Can you help us build houses?
DIY teacher:	Yes, of course.

They go off together to make their houses. Then another pupil goes across stage with clock/sign saying "Three hours later". Pigs bring their model houses on.

DIY teacher:	See, you are very good at making things.
Pigs:	Thank you very much, Sir.

Scene 3

At home
Pigs go off and reappear with model houses hidden behind their backs and head for home where they find Mum and Dad relaxing and looking surprised to see them. They jump up, hastily hiding wine!

Mum:	You're back! *(Not very pleased!)*
Pigs:	Yes.
Dad:	What have you learnt?
Pigs:	Maths, music, sport, history and DIY!
Mum:	DIY? *(Looks pleased)*
Pigs:	Yes, here are our houses! *(They show model houses)*
Mum:	They are ... very ... beautiful. *(Starts enthusiastically but voice tails off. She's not really very happy to see them!)*

Pigs go off looking happy

Mum and Dad:	Oh no, they're never going to leave home!

Pigs come back singing

Pigs:	Who's afraid of the big bad wolf?
	In any case, it's definitely not us!

The End

Dorothy goes shopping (Dorothée fait les courses)

Scene 1

At the farm
Aunt Emma, Uncle and two farmhands are already on stage as Dorothy arrives

Emma:	Dorothy, Dorothy, where are you?
Dorothy:	Hi, I'm here!
Emma:	Where have you been?
Dorothy:	I went to the shops (like you asked me to).
Emma:	What did you buy?
Dorothy:	I bought cheese, butter, ham ... .
Emma:	*(Increasingly cross)* And the tomatoes? The apples? The mushrooms?
Dorothy:	Oh no. I forgot them. I am sorry. *(Pauses)* Don't worry. I'll go and fetch some from the market.

Dorothy starts to move away from centre stage as if she is going to go back to the shops.
Uncle and two silly farmhands look at the sky and discuss impending tornado, finally looking scared

Uncle:	No, Dorothy, it's very windy, it's too dangerous.
Farmhand 1:	Look at the sky.
Farmhand 2:	It doesn't look good.
Farmhand 1:	It doesn't look good at all.
Farmhand 2:	Is there a tornado coming?
Farmhand 1:	I think so ... I'm scared.
Farmhand 2:	Help!

Farmhands run around and look scared, Uncle looks irritated

Uncle:	Oh, my Goodness!
Dorothy:	Bye. I'll be back in five minutes.
Uncle:	No, wait! *(Uncle tries to stop her but isn't quick enough)*

Scene 2

En route
All exit stage except Dorothy who wanders back and forth as if she is going back to the shops, then the tornado arrives – most of the cast whirl around her pretending to be tornado, she finally collapses and falls asleep, they drop green tickets all around her. She wakes up and picks up a ticket

Dorothy:	*(Yawns)* What's this? *(Pauses and holds up ticket)* Emerald City shopping centre ... half price sales ... fifty per cent off. *(Very enthusiastic – she loves sales!)* Great! I love sales!

Skips off singing to tune of the French National Anthem

Dorothy:	So, let's go to the shopping mall,
	The day of shopping has arrived.

Scarecrow comes on from other side and stands still in typical pose. Witch also comes on, rubs hands together excitedly

Witch: Half price sales? I'm coming too. *(Then goes off, cackling)* Ha, ha, ha ... .

After a pause Dorothy comes on and notices Scarecrow

Dorothy: Excuse me, where is the Emerald City shopping centre, please?

Scarecrow: It's that way. *(Swings hands left, then right, Dorothy notices)*

Dorothy: Is it this way or that way? *(Becoming slightly cross, points left then right)*

Scarecrow: It's that way. *(Swings arms across each other to point in both directions)*

Dorothy: *(Really cross)* This is ridiculous and you are stupid!

Scarecrow: Yes, I am very stupid ... . I haven't got a brain.

Dorothy: You haven't got a brain?! *(Surprised, but not cross now, pauses, walks away then comes back)*

Do you like shopping?

Scarecrow: *(Scratches his head and answers hesitantly)* Yes ... . No ... . Er ... . I don't know!

Dorothy: *(Firmly)* Come to the shopping centre. We're going to buy a brain.

They go off singing 'So, let's go to the shopping mall' as before, then come back on. Next they find Lion crying by a tree frightened by Mouse

Dorothy: What's the matter? Are you frightened of a mouse?

Lion: Yes I haven't got any courage.

Mouse: *(Threatens lion)* Your money or your life?!

Lion: The money, the money, don't kill me!

Lion tries to give purse to Mouse, but Dorothy stops him and takes him by the hand

Dorothy: No! Come shopping with us. We'll buy some courage.

Scarecrow: Boo!! *(To Mouse)*

They go off singing as before. They come across the Tin Man

Tin Man: Excuse me, are you going to the shopping centre?

Dorothy: Yes. What are you looking for?

Tin Man: I'd like to buy a heart ... because ... I haven't got one!

Dorothy: Poor you. Come with us.

Witch creeps back across the stage unnoticed

Witch:	*(Scornfully)* And I'm going to buy hearts and brains to make soup!

Scene 3

In the Emerald shopping centre
They sing again and arrive at the Emerald shopping centre. They look excited when they see the sign

Dorothy, Scarecrow, Lion and Tin Man:	*(Singing)* Shopping centre, we have arrived! Wallets at the ready!

Stallholders trying to sell their fruit/bread/flowers to the four friends

Stallholder 1:	*(Loudly)* Peaches, pears, oranges.
Scarecrow:	Oh no, they're rotten.
Stallholder 2:	Lovely fresh bread ... croissants ... cakes.
Lion:	Too expensive.
Stallholder 3:	Buy your flowers here: roses, violets, tulips. *(Points to old dying flowers)*
Tin Man:	They are dead! *(Looks shocked)*
Dorothy, Scarecow and Lion:	Dead! *(They all gasp loudly and make cross sign)*

Pause

Lion:	Where are we going to buy courage, a brain and a heart?
Tin Man:	I don't know ... . There's nothing here.
Scarecrow:	What would you like to buy, Dorothy?
Dorothy:	I'm looking for shoes ... red shoes.

Witch overhears this and creeps across back of stage again

Witch:	Shoes! I love shoes ... but I haven't got any money. *(Pulls out empty pockets)*
Stallholder 4:	Courage, courage, come and buy your courage here.

All four friends jump up in excitement

Dorothy:	Courage! Lion, go and buy some courage. *(Urges him on)*
Lion:	Oh no, I'm too scared.
Scarecrow:	Go on Lion, buy some courage! *(Speaks firmly, pushes Lion forward)*
Lion:	No, I can't. It's too expensive ... it's dangerous!

Magician arrives dramatically

Magician:	Can I help you?
Lion:	I need some courage but I don't want to buy it. The

	stallholder is very scary.
Magician:	*(Waves wand around pretending to do magic)* Abracadabra!
Lion:	*(Lion not so scared now magic has worked)* How much is the courage?
Stallholder 4:	One euro.
Lion:	One euro. It's not expensive at all. *Lion pays money, stallholder gives him courage in a box which he swallows. He instantly flexes his muscles and goes up to all the stallholders)* Boo, boo, boo!
Stallholder 5:	Brains for sale. Come and get your brains here. Small ones, big ones!
Dorothy:	Go and buy a brain! *(Dorothy urges Scarecrow to buy a brain)*

Scarecrow looks at all the brains, picking them up and commenting on them

Scarecrow:	This one's too big … . This one's too small … . This one's perfect! Does it suit me?

Pretends to try it on his head, it breaks through hole in his old hat

Dorothy:	Yes, it's great!

Scarecrow hands over the money, gets his brain and does intelligent things, like reading newspaper

Tin Girl:	Hearts for sale!

Dorothy hears and nudges Tin Man

Dorothy:	Go and buy a heart.
Tin Girl:	Pink hearts, purple hearts, not expensive at all. 50 percent reduction.

Witch creeps up behind and secretly steals purse from Tin Man's pocket. Magician notices.
Tin Man sees Tin Girl and feels shy as he likes her

Tin Girl:	Do you want to buy a heart?
Tin Man:	Yes … no … . *(Turns to the others)* She is very beautiful!
Dorothy:	Go on! *(Encourages him)*
Tin Girl:	Only four euros!
Tin Man:	*(Tries to find money)* I've lost my money.
Tin Girl:	It doesn't matter. You are very handsome. I'll give it to you! *(They look lovingly at each other!)*

Magician catches Witch and gets her to hand over the purse

Magician:	*(To Witch)* The purse! Have you lost something? *(Hands purse back to Tin Man)*
Tin Man:	Yes, my purse … . Ah thank you!

Tin Man and Tin Girl look happy together. Magician takes Witch off

Dorothy and Scarecrow:	It must be love! Aahh!
Stallholder 6:	Shoes for sale, pretty shoes!

Dorothy jumps up excitedly

Dorothy:	Have you got any red shoes?
Stallholder 6:	Yes, what size are you?
Dorothy:	Thirty seven ... . Thank you ... they are very pretty.

Dorothy and others sit down pleased. She speaks to each friend in turn

Dorothy: So, you've got your brain, you've got your courage, you've got your heart and I've got my shoes. I think I can go home now.

Puts on shoes and finds they are magical

Dorothy: The shoes are magic.
There's no place like home! *(x 3)*

Dorothy spins off, they all wave goodbye

All: Goodbye Dorothy

The End

Lightning Source UK Ltd.
Milton Keynes UK
UKOW07f1935031017

310345UK00001B/1/P

9 781783 172450